INSECT MAN

INSECT MAN

A Fight Against Malaria in Africa

ALEC SMITH

The Radcliffe Press
London · New York

This book is dedicated with all my love
to my wife, Irene,
and daughters, Linda and Diana

Published in 1993 by
The Radcliffe Press
45 Bloomsbury Square
London WC1A 2HY

175 Fifth Avenue
New York
NY 10010

In the United States of America
and Canada distributed by
St Martin's Press
175 Fifth Avenue
New York
NY 10010

A CIP record for this book is
available from the British Library

A full CIP record is available
from the Library of Congress

ISBN 1-85043-597-9

Photoset in North Wales by
Derek Doyle & Associates, Mold, Clwyd
Printed and bound in Great Britain by
WBC Ltd, Bridgend, Mid-Glamorgan

Contents

General Foreword
to the Series

A.H.M. KIRK-GREENE

Lecturer in the Modern History of Africa, University of Oxford, and
formerly of the Colonial Administrative Service, Nigeria.

A whole generation has passed, nearer two in the case of the Asian sub-continent, since Britain's colonial territories in South-East Asia, Africa and the Caribbean, achieved independence. In the Pacific the transfer of power came about a decade later. There was little interest in recording the official or the personal experience of empire either in the inter-war years – viewed by some, often among those personally involved, as the apogee of the British empire – or in the immediate aftermath of empire. And in this latter period attitudes were critical, largely condemnatory and even positively hostile. This is not surprising: such a reaction is usual at the end of a remarkable period of history.

With the passing of time and with longer historical perspective it was possible to see events in a better and more objective light and the trend was gradually reversed. In due course there came about a more sympathetic interest in the colonial period, both by those in Britain or in the countries of the former empire who were intrigued to know how colonial government operated – in local, everyday practice, as well as at the policy level of the Colonial Office and Government House. Furthermore, those who had themselves been an integral part of the process wanted to record the experience before, in the nature of things, it was too late. Here was a potentially rich vein of knowledge and personal experience for specialist academic historians as well as the general reader.

Leaving aside the extensive academic analysis of the end of empire, the revival of interest in the colonial period in this country may be said to have been stimulated by creative literature. In the

late 1960s there were novels, films, radio and TV programmes now
and again tinged with a touch of nineteenth-century romance and
with just a whiff of nostalgia to soften the sharp realism of the
colonial encounter. The focus was primarily on India and the
post-1947 imagery of the 'Raj': there were outstanding novels by
Paul Scott – surely destined to be one of the greatest
twentieth-century novelists – J. G. Farrell and John Masters; epic
films like *A Passage to India*, and *Gandhi*, or the charming and
moving vignette of *Staying On*, and, for Africa, *Out of Africa* and
Mister Johnson.

In the second half of the 1970s there emerged a highly successful
genre of collective 'colonial' memoirs in the *Tales of ...* format:
Charles Allen's splendid trilogy *Plain Tales from the Raj* (1975),
Tales from the Dark Continent (1979) and *Tales from the South
China Seas* (1983), followed by others like *Tales of Paradise:
Memories of the British in the South Pacific* (1986) and *Tales of
Empire: the British in the Middle East* (1989) all good history and
good reading.

Throughout the period from India's independence until that of
the last crown colony there had, of course, been those splendid
works which combined both academic history and creative
literature: for example, Philip Woodruff's *The Men Who Rules
India: The Founders* (1953) and *The Guardians* (1954); and Jan
Morris's *Heaven's Command, Pax Britannica* and *Farewell the
Trumpets* (1973–8).

Finally as the 1970s gave way to the 1980s, those voices which
had remained largely silent since the end of empire now wanted to
be heard. The one-time colonial officials, be they district officers,
agriculturalists, veterinary, medical or forestry officers, policemen
or magistrates, and just as often their wives, began to write about
their experiences. They wrote with relish and enthusiasm, with a
touch of adventure and few personal regrets. There was a common
feeling of a practical and useful task well done, although some
thought that more could have been achieved had independence
come about more slowly.

These memoirs often began as little more than a private record
for the family, children and grandchildren, some of whom had
never seen a colonial governor in full fig, shaken hands with an emir

or paramount chief, discussed plans with a peasant or local politician, or known at first hand the difference between an *askari* and *alkali*, an *amah* and an *ayah*. By 1990, the colonial memoir had begun to establish itself as a literary genre in its own right.

The initiative of the Radcliffe Press in harnessing and promoting this talent, primarily autobiographical but also biographical, promises to be a positive addition to both the historical and literary scenes. Here is a voice from the last Colonial Service generation, relating from personal experience the lives and careers involved in the exercise of latter-day empire. They were part of what was arguably the most influential and far-reaching international event of the second half of the twentieth century, namely the end of empire and the consequent emergence of the independent nations of the Third World. It could perhaps also be argued that this is part of an even greater process – decolonization 'writ large', a sea-change in world affairs affecting greater and lesser powers into the late twentieth century.

It may well be that by 2066, the centenary of the closing down of the Colonial Office, great-great-grandchildren will find the most telling image of Britain's third and final empire in these authentic memoirs and biographical studies, rather than in the weightier imperial archives at the Public Record Office at Kew or in Rhodes House Library, Oxford.

Foreword

I stress that throughout this book all opinions and judgements are mine alone, and do not represent the views or policies of any official body, including the World Health Organization (WHO), or the various national governments and services with whom I had contact.

Acknowledgements

The author wishes to thank Mr S. Calabar-Oviawe of the University of Benin, Benin City, Edo State, Nigeria, for permission to publish the photograph on the jacket of the book, and also to Umegbe Village Community and especially to Chief Amadasun for their co-operation with the photography. Grateful thanks are also due to Mr Duncan Whitfield, FMPA, for permission to use his photographs as plates 2, 3, 4 and 5 of the picture section. Every effort has been made to avoid any infringement of copyright in the use of photographs and to acknowledge picture sources. If any omission has been unintentionally made, the publishers will be pleased to rectify the error in a subsequent edition of the book.

1

Outward Bound

I have always wanted to be a naturalist as far back as I can remember. As a child I lived opposite a wonderful oak wood alive with birds and small mammals. Nearby was another wood with a pond which, in season, teamed with spawning frogs and newts. It was also rich in sticklebacks and minnows, and it supported a fine variety of insects, notably dragon-flies, water scorpions and water boatmen. My home, appropriately named 'Woodcroft', had a sizeable garden and a small orchard, both of which hosted an astonishing diversity of insect pests.

I was born in 'Woodcroft' and lived there until the Second World War broke out twelve years later. From this home, situated in what was then rural Great Barr on the northern outskirts of Birmingham, I was evacuated to the delightfully even more rural town of Ashby-de-la-Zouch in Leicestershire. In this setting my interest in animals of the countryside, particularly birds, grew. This was just as well for I was scholastically as thick as two short planks until reaching the fifth form, my main interests being playing rugby and exploring the surrounding countryside in companionship with school friends. Following a bet for the then princely sum of ten shillings, made with schoolfriend John Philpot, during the severely cold winter of 1941/42, Calvin Round and I broke a patch of ice and swam in nearby Willesden Lake. The following morning I caught pneumonia but pulled through, largely due to care and attention given by my housemaster, Mr. Eric Pedley, and his wife Kate. Shortly afterwards, I was awarded the newly created 'Aston Badge' for the most popular boy in the school as judged by pupils and staff.

Biology was not included in the fifth form curriculum of my school in 1943, when I took School Certificate. However, because of my interest in this subject I was permitted to take the exam and passed at credit level. This modest achievement fuelled my enthusiasm and, with generous provision of laboratory material and bench space by the headmaster, I studied for and took Higher School Certificate in botany and zoology without tutorial assistance. I also took chemistry under normal tuition and in 1945 passed HSC well enough to be awarded the School Temperly Science Prize and to gain entrance to the University of Birmingham to study Zoology and Comparative Physiology. I also received school rugby colours, having played at right prop in the first team since the third form. My schooldays at King Edward VI Grammar School in Aston, Birmingham, in 1938–45, particularly as an evacuee, thus provided many opportunities which encouraged my interest in natural history.

My undergraduate days, 1945–48, were much less eventful than my schooldays. I read zoology as principal subject with chemistry and human physiology as subsidiaries. I enjoyed squash and played many games with Dennis Noble, with whom I was partner during the bench work in human physiology. I also enjoyed swimming, and was captain of the zoology department basketball team. Indeed, I enjoyed sports so much that during my first year I even thought of leaving zoology for the newly established department of physical education. Many of my fellow zoology students aspired to be teachers, but Desmond Morris showed an interest in mammals and I enjoyed discussions on marine biology and insect behaviour with a young lecturer, Laurie Finlayson.

At the end of my final year, with Professor Peter Medawar as Head of Department, I was awarded First Class Honours in Zoology, followed by the offer of a Colonial Medical Research studentship at The London School of Hygiene and Tropical Medicine for two years. I received training in tropical medical entomology and was assigned a small research project under Professor P.A. Buxton. At the end of this period, I was awarded a Ph.D. and published a small paper on 'The effect of relative humidity on behaviour of the tropical rat flea *Xenopsylla cheopis*'. Living in London was a useful experience. I first lodged near

Queens Gate and then in Baker Street but found it too expensive for my grant of £300 per year. I then lodged at Barons Court at less expense. The perfect place as found towards the end of the first year when three of us, Tom Fletcher, John Sudd and myself – all post-graduate students at The London School – shared lodgings in Camden Town at thirty shillings per week each. I joined the Y.M.C.A. in Great Russell Street and played rugby for the first or second teams as opportunities arose. I also enjoyed the other ammenities of the Y.M.C.A., including swimming, catch-as-catch can and judo wrestling. I also did a bit of rock climbing with London University mountaineering club.

In June 1950, I was called to the Colonial Office in Great Smith Street to be interviewed by Dr. L. Lewthwaite, Director of The Colonial Medical Research Service. He explained that this service was based in the U.K. and that its staff could expect continuity of service, but with transfer from one colony or territory to another as research requirements dictated. This much appealed to me, for not only did it involve travel to foreign parts, but it also held promise of actually working in different countries scattered across the globe. This promise was further strengthened when he then offered me the post of entomologist with the newly established Filariasis Research Unit based in Tanganyika Territory within the administrative umbrella of the East African High Commission whose headquarters were centred in Nairobi, Kenya. *Bancroftial filariasis* is distributed worldwide within the tropics and transmitted by several species of mosquitoes. It seemed that impetus had been given to the study of this already acknowledged serious disease by quite a number of American troops acquiring the infection during service in the Western Pacific. I accepted the offer with no regard whatsoever for salary or conditions of service. Not surprisingly, I commenced my career the following month at £500 per year (i.e., at the bottom of the Scientific Officer scale) instead of a couple of increments up, which would probably have been granted had I requested them in respect of my two years spent on post-graduate studies. My status as a bachelor was considered advantageous for an officer on first tour. Young married personnel were not encouraged to take their wives out first tour since they needed this period to find if they could fit in to a colonial life-style, and also to learn enough of the customs and language of the indigenous people to work effectively and support a wife under tropical, and frequently quite primitive, conditions. The opportunity was also taken to inform me in no uncertain terms that malaria was an avoidable risk in view of the ready availability of synthetic anti-malaria drugs such as paludrine and chloroquine.

Passage to Africa was by sea, in line with normal travel arrangements of that time, and I was booked on the Union Castle Line vessel, the *Good Hope Castle*, due to leave London docks towards the end of August 1950. It was planned that I would disembark at the capital and chief port of Tanganyika, Dar-es-Salaam, and travel up country by rail to my duty station, Mwanza. With my Ph.D, colonial appointment, and passage arrangements behind me, I had about a month in which to read more about *Bancroftial filariasis*, and prepare myself generally for travel to Tanganyika. One of the great features of working at the London School of Hygiene and Tropical Medicine was the constant flow in and out of tropical workers, either recently returned from duty overseas or preparing for another tour, often involving a change of country. Another feature was the morning and afternoon tea breaks held in the Department of Entomology. These were quite short but of great value to staff, the eight or so post-graduate students, and visiting workers from overseas. Conversation was encouraged by Professor Buxton provided that it was of a broadly professional nature. I took these opportunities to talk to entomologists then working in Tanganyika. Comments were generally less than glowing. 'Africa is a disappointing continent' was expressed by one who had transferred from India following its independence in 1947. Others considered Kenya to be God's Own Country, but neighbouring Tanganyika too harsh for happy married life. The abundance and variety of game was mentioned and the glorious sunsets over Lake Victoria. 'Take a metal trunk,' said one, who knew someone who had gone on safari in Tanganyika and found on return that the termites had penetrated his wooden trunk and eaten the contents. The best advice given was to buy a camera, for this could frequently be of great professional use for recording habitats of mosquitoes and situations in which disease was transmitted, and could also be useful for indicating the conditions under which one was living. I passed the obligatory medical examination and prepared for the great unknown by purchasing a metal trunk and a Retina IIa camera, as well as taking a supply of anti-malaria tablets and receiving yellow fever and cholera jabs.

In the decade 1940–1950, boy usually met girl at a public dance. I was no exception, except that it happened only a few weeks before departure. I had been to the Y.M.C.A. for a relaxing swim, following an afternoon playing rugby, and on leaving saw a notice on the Y.W.C.A. building opposite to the effect that a splendid dance was to be held there that evening. I went along. There was a good attendance. A dance had just finished and many people were sitting waiting for the next dance. When the music struck up I asked one of the sitting ladies for a dance. We had barely commenced dancing when I realized that I was smitten, the classic *coup de foudre* or love at first sight. She was charming, vivacious and extremely attractive. I was captivated in her aura of pheronomes. In this way I met Miss Irene Forsdike. Fortunately, I had not as yet purchased several items of clothing recommended by the colonial office, and I was more than delighted when Irene agreed to help me shop for evening dress. The following weekend we went to Simpson's and bought a black evening dress suit and a white sharkskin evening jacket. Thereafter I lived in a haze waiting for our next meeting. We went to F.P. Bakers, the tropical outfitters, where I bought a camp bed and mosquito-net. She helped me with further shopping and within a few days she must have known that I was dotty over her. We went to the theatre, cinema, dances and walks, and I kissed her whenever the slightest opportunity arose.

In retrospect, I should have asked her to marry me there and then, and taken a chance on the reaction of the Colonial Office. However, with only a fortnight to go before embarkation, it seemed to me that the die was cast and, in any case, at the back of my mind lay the thought that there must have been a sound basis for earlier advice given me at the Colonial Office not to take one's wife out on first tour. As we shall see later, this advice turned out to be well founded. We did not become engaged, but had an understanding and wrote to each other frequently until I returned on home leave three years later to commence a wonderful and eventful marriage to

Irene which continues to this day.

One day, in the last week of August 1950, I set off from the London School of Hygiene and Tropical Medicine, with my briefcase containing notes on *filariasis* and keys for the identification of mosquitoes, and on meeting a colleague, Dr. Mick Gillies, I called out, 'I'm off to Africa today'. This remark, and the circumstances, clearly amused him so much that in later years he was often wont to tell this tale. I arrived at King George V docks by taxi and boarded the merchant vessel *Good Hope Castle* just in time to see my metal trunk lowered into one of the holds. As it landed with a thump the welding or soldering along the bottom of the trunk gave way on all sides. Fortunately, the bottom was held securely in place by some 120 ft of nylon climbing rope which I had wound round the trunk due to shortage of space within it. This experience taught me never to use metal trunks again, since not only could they split, but they were also greatly disliked by dockers who preferred wooden trunks into which they could get their steel hooks, thus protecting their hands. The ship left dock on the high tide that evening, starting me off on a career extending over thirty years working in Africa south of the Sahara.

The *Good Hope Castle* was quite small, having a displacement of just over 9,000 tons. It was a one-class ship with about thirty passengers, mostly colonial officers and their wives returning to the Sudan, Kenya or Tanganyika after home leave. I shared a cabin with two officers of the East Africa Postal and Telegraph Department whose headquarters was Nairobi, and one officer of the East African Railways and Harbours stationed in Mombassa. My three companions were seasoned colonials who, like me, were on the staff of East African High Commission organizations (i.e., institutes or departments that served the three countries of Kenya, Tanganyika and Uganda). Cabin space was a bit cramped but I never found the expression one sometimes encountered of 'Union Cattle Line' really justified. Compared with austerity Britain, which was probably in its lowest trough in the 1950s with quite stringent food rationing, each meal on the *Good Hope Castle* seemed a banquet. The passengers were a lively lot, frequently supporting the bar in animated discussion. I joined them whenever I could, which was only very occasionally, as I was extremely hard up having nearly exhausted my savings kitting myself out and wooing Irene. During much of the three weeks voyage I passed time learning Swahili, the coastal and trade language used by Africans throughout East Africa. I used the standard book of those times (i.e. Steere's 'Swahili Exercises') and tried to learn ten different words each day.

Our first port of call was Gibraltar for a few hours extending over a late afternoon and evening. My cabin companions and I, along with several passengers from other ships, wandered up the high street to see the sights. There was a notable smart British atmosphere conveyed by police and military uniforms and characteristic pillar boxes on street corners. The atmosphere in the couple of cafe-bars that we visited was, however, very different. In the first one, we had barely sat down to our drinks when there was a clattering of castanets and in swept half a dozen or so less than attractive flamenco dancing girls. We watched for a few minutes and then continued our walk up the high street until we came to a somewhat more presentable cafe-bar from which emanated popular dance music. Once again, we had hardly ordered our drinks when in swept the same group of flamenco dancers. This time they invited us to dance with them ballroom style. My partner was a good dancer but towards the end of the dance asked me if I would like to marry her for the night. I firmly, but quite civilly, declined, and as soon as our dance ended returned to ship along with the other passengers.

Next port of call was Port Said at the mouth of the Suez Canal. Our vessel was besieged with vendors arriving by all sorts of small craft loaded with brassware, pouffes, camelbags, rugs, carved and inlaid boxes, and a vast variety of glittering trinkets. This was quite entertaining but I was strapped for cash and could not afford to buy anything. It was amongst these vendors that I first heard and understood a word in the Swahili language: 'Subulkheri,' said one to another. This brought home to me that Swahili, although very largely a Bantu language, was enriched by other languages, notably Arabic. Africans of Mohammedan faith would thus often greet each other with 'subulkheri' for 'good morning', instead of the Bantu expression, 'habari asubuhi'. A very clever exhibition of conjuring with newly hatched chickens was given on board by two local 'galley-galley' men.

After two days in Port Said we left Suez at the southern end of the

Insect Man

canal. The air was breathless and temperatures on board were close
to 40 degrees centigrade. Apart from a small, timber-floored
area around the cabin, the deck of the vessel was of iron with
much of that covered in cargo. The crew found a space and
constructed what they were pleased to call a swimming pool. It
comprised a canvas sack filled with sea water and could
accommodate two or three people standing, but there was no room
for swimming.There was no air-conditioning aboard and the
outside air ducted into the cabins gave little relief from the heat.
When we arrived at Port Suez I was therefore very pleased when the
opportunity came for us to go ashore to stretch our legs. My cabin
companions and I strolled round the port area looking at some of
the already familiar wares for sale. During this stroll, a local
teenage boy sidled along inviting us to meet his sister who was 'very
nice, very clean, all pink inside'. His invitation had no appeal
whatsoever and we told him in no uncertain terms to push off.

Our next port of call was Port Sudan, about half way down the
Red Sea. We docked there for five interminable days of oppressive
heat, watching bales of cotton being loaded on board. My
companions, who were due to disembark at the next port,
Mombasa, made a very good case for me also to disembark at
Mombasa instead of Dar-es-Salaam. The main appeal was that I
would get to my duty station, Mwanza, about a week earlier by
cutting out three or four days docking in Mombasa and probably a
couple of days in Zanzibar. Accordingly, I disembarked at
Mombasa, staying overnight in the 'Manor Hotel', a white
colonnaded stucco building in the flower of colonial architecture.
The rooms were large, clean and relatively cool compared with on
board ship. The manager was a European, and the servants
impressive in their white 'kanzu' uniforms with red cumberbands
and fezes. Male servants were addressed as 'boy' irrespective of age.
I inflicted some of my two-hundred word Swahili vocabulary on the
servants. My pronunciation was execrable as I had not yet learned
to deepen my voice or to emphasize the penultimate syllable.
Nevertheless, there was some impact as I heard one 'boy' say to
another, 'Anasema swahili kidogo hata alifika leo tu' (i.e., 'He
speaks a little Swahili even though he only arrived today). I
eschewed dinner that evening but had a splendid breakfast next day

20

before leaving for Mwanza. The dining room looked as if it were spread out for a banquet. Long tables around the walls, covered in full white tablecloths, supported numerous bowls of luscious fruit: bananas of different varieties, some even with red skins; tangerines; oranges, some with orange but most with green skins; mangoes; and the most magnificent pineapples. I was placed at a table opposite a living characterization of an old colonial. When the 'boy' approached, bearing starters comprising thick segments of pawpaw with a slice of lime fruit, the old colonial turned puce and shouted, 'Take that pap away!'. I enjoyed the pawpaw very much and the full English breakfast, reflecting how different even breakfasts were from the austere England that I had just left.

I journeyed from Mombasa to Nairobi by train in company with my cabin companion who worked with East African Railways and Harbours. It was a steam train with three classes, based solely on degrees of comfort and other facilities but with big differences in cost, so that most Europeans and the wealthier Asians travelled first class, as did a very few Africans. The second class was largely used by Asians and less affluent Europeans, and the third class was used almost entirely by Africans. My companion and I had warrants for first class travel. Seated nearby were three young Seychelles women. They were colourfully and smartly dressed and spoke a slightly high-pitched, accented English so loudly that the whole carriage was privy to their conversation. Meals were not included, although costs would have been refunded against receipts. I ate inexpensively and skipped a few meals. The train stopped at several stations and when we reached Nairobi my companion departed and I stayed on till the train reached its terminus, Kisumu, in the Western Province of Kenya and situated on the north east shore of Lake Victoria. I recalled that it was here that Speke, the nineteenth century explorer, first saw the Lake and realized that he had found the source of the mighty Nile river.

By the greatest fortune, the lake steamer *Tilapia* docked at Kisumu within a few hours of my arrival. The upper deck was fully booked with Europeans but I was able to get a place among the African passengers on the lower deck at the stern of the vessel. There was no difficulty in getting a warrant as the lake steamer service was an East African High Commission service directly managed by E.A. Railways and Harbours. There were two lake steamers which sailed round Lake Victoria in a clockwise direction, taking five days to complete the circle. These steamers had an attractive Edwardian appearance and were of undoubted antiquity, having been brought up from the coast and assembled at Kisumu. They were essentially small merchant vessels which could berth about ten passengers. Hence a trip round Lake Victoria was quite popular among Europeans taking local leave. From Kisumu, the *Tilapia* sailed south down the east coast of the lake, stopping at Musoma to collect bales of cotton. It then carefully navigated the Rugeye Channel, which is situated between Ukerewe Island and Ukerewe Mainland, and proceeded on to Mwanza at the southern end of the Lake.

I was delighted to get on board, and, from the deck, see people of different tribes, tropical vegetation and wild animals. The people were largely Wanyamwesi and Basukuma from the Lake Province of Tanganyika. Much of the vegetation at the lakeside was papyrus interspersed with water lettuce, which in some areas of the lake supported enormous numbers of non-malarious but extremely vicious biting mosquitoes. Indeed, on the mainland bank of the Rugeye Channel there was a large notice painted with the warning 'HATARI:MBU' (i.e., Danger! Mosquitoes). The lakeside bird life was fascinating. Flocks of white egrets, hammercocks, and smaller numbers of the magnificent kavirondo crane would come into view, while the branches of many trees overhanging the lake's edge were filled with weaver birds and their nests. There were many large rocks in the lake, and on some of them crocodiles could be seen basking in the sun with their mouths open. A few hippos also appeared, with their eyes and ears just showing above the water.

The 'Tilapia' arrived at Mwanza just before nightfall. I disembarked hungry, thirsty, but not quite penniless: I still had fifteen cents. The 'Mwanza Hotel', which was near to the port, gave me accommodation for the night and the next morning I presented myself at the East African Filariasis Research Unit. The first staff member I met was Mr. Rhodes Jones who predictably exclaimed, 'Good God, we didn't expect you for a week!'

2

Ukara Island

M wanza was a very small town, with the central shopping area having European features such as colonnaded verandahs, but its overall appearance was Asian and Islamic, due to details in its building design, a predominant mosque, and the loud and interminable strains of Indian music. It was quite an attractive town, with most buildings in the centre having cream-distempered or whitewashed walls and corrugated iron roofs which had been painted red. The roads, of red latteritic earth, were lined with flamboyant trees whose branches were covered in red blossom between September and December. Its situation on the lake's edge made it particularly attractive in the evenings when magnificent sunsets were reflected on the lake.

The township population was largely African of the Basukuma tribe, which is the largest in Tanganyika. The Africans either lived in groups of huts on the outskirts of town or in 'boys' quarters' attached to individual houses within the town. Indians, whether Hindus or Sikhs, formed the second largest segment of township population, many living above their own shops in the town centre. The Europeans, possibly about two hundred and fifty all told, were mainly British, with a few Italians and Greeks. Most British were Tanganyika civil servants. Those in government administration were said to work in the 'boma', which comprised a group of offices surrounding a courtyard: they included the Provincial and District Commissioners. The others mostly worked in the Public Works Department, the Department of Health, or the Department of Agriculture. A few represented the commercial sector, including

23

banks and the marketing of cotton, which was an important crop grown in the Lake Province. While there were no formal social barriers, there was generally little social mixing between Europeans, Asians and Africans. There was a lively 'European' club, joined by all but a few Europeans, and a considerable amount of private entertainment at people's homes, much of this between members of the same department.

My director, Colonel William Laurie, had the formidable task of establishing a Filariasis Research Unit and a Medical Survey Unit, and was much involved in planning and overviewing the siting, construction and furnishing of laboratories, offices and housing for his staff, and the purchase of laboratory equipment and appropriate vehicles and vessels. I was introduced to other staff including Medical Officer, Dr. Trant, Medical Research Officer, Dr. Peter Jordan, and Parasitologist, Dr. Peter Sewell. Considerable research was required in the field and in the laboratory to ascertain whether *Bancroftial filariasis* could best be controlled by treating infected people with drugs such as diethylcarbamazine or by controlling the mosquitoes transmitting the disease. The research programme assigned to me was to find out which species of mosquitoes transmitted *Bancroftial filariasis*, and indicate how best these mosquitoes could be controlled. In the late 1940s, geographically isolated islands such as Cyprus, Sardinia and Mauritius had been selected for malaria eradication trials using insecticides, with extremely successful results. Ukara Island, in Lake Victoria, was therefore selected for in-depth studies on the transmission of *Bancroftial filariasis*, which was present in twenty one per cent of its human population.

I spent the first three months in Mwanza settling in. During this period, I was accommodated in the Mwanza Hotel as no housing was available. It was a small hotel with whitewashed walls and corrugated iron roof which formed a huge sounding board during the rains, rendering normal conversation almost impossible. There was feeble electric lighting throughout, and overhead fans in the lounge and dining room, but, as a newcomer, I found it pretty hot and humid indoors in the evenings. A German manageress ran the hotel efficiently and I enjoyed the meals, including the many fish dishes prepared with locally caught lake fish, particularly the Nile perch. I was introduced to that great East African institution, the weekend curry lunch washed down with generous libations of cold I.P.A. beer. Another favourite of mine was the banana fritter. As an important customer of many of the general stores, the manageress attracted a roomful of presents well in advance of Christmas, and she did not hesitate to demand changes where there was unwanted duplication.

I went through the necessary rounds of introductions, meeting the District Commissioner, Medical Officer in charge of the European hospital, bank manager, and secretary of the club, all of whom were British, and managers of the principal shops, all of whom were Indian. As befitted a colonial officer on first tour, my reception was civil but perfunctory, with the exception of the secretary of the club. On learning that I enjoyed swimming, I was nominated and elected swimming member, a position that the club had great difficulty in filling. Whether this was due to fear of catching bilharzia or being eaten by crocodiles was not made apparent at the time. The club had a swimming enclosure on the shore of Lake Victoria. It was about twenty five feet square, fenced off by iron railings, and on the shore was a thatched hut which served as a dressing room. With the help of a 'fundi', (i.e. an expert, in this case a Sikh carpenter and metalworker), I carried out the very few repairs required to exclude crocodiles. The concern about bilharzia was more difficult to resolve since there was no information, at that time, about the transmission of bilharzia along the lake shore in the Mwanza area. I searched the water edge of the swimming enclosure to the depth of about two feet but could find no snails, bilharzia or otherwise. This information was passed on to the club committee and allayed the fears of some club members but by no means all of them.

I took to life in the tropics like a duck to water and during the few months I spent in Mwanza participated in the social life as far as practicable. This included an occasional game of soccer and hockey, both of which were new to me. Indeed, during my first game of hockey it was not until well after half time that I realized that the referee's cry of 'Sticks' was directed at me. Hunting was a popular sport in the Lake Province. Crocodiles were considered vermin, and as well as providing sport were also shot for the commercial value of their skins. Some professional hunters favoured an 8 mm. calibre rifle for shooting crocodile and general game. Accordingly, when a second hand one was offered to me for two hundred shillings, I jumped at it. The rifle was a beautiful old breech-loading Mauser with an octagonal barrel. Some days later, I realized that the rifling was rather worn and consequently rarely used it, but it was a splendid collectors' piece and I never replaced it. The Lake Province had an abundance and wide variety of game birds such as guinea fowl, yellow necked partridge, sand grouse and Nile duck. The gun most widely used for shooting birds was the .22 rifle for which cartridges of different types were available, ranging from bird shot to high velocity, the latter often used for shooting small ungulates such as dik-dik, duiker and Thompson's gazelle. I purchased a new Czechoslovakian Brno .22 five-shot magazine-loading rifle from a local shop and used it quite frequently for almost ten years. The general game licence, purchased for thirty shillings, permitted the holder to shoot a restricted number of plains game such as eland, hartebeest, topi, waterbuck, wildebeest, warthog, Thompson's and Grant's gazelles, impala, and dik-dik, as well as unlimited numbers of most game birds. Hunting was restricted to certain areas, the most popular one near Mwanza being some one hundred and forty miles away up the eastern shore of the lake near the Serengeti game reserve. I went on two or three hunting expeditions and then lost interest, as I did not need the game meat and I became deeply involved in preparing for working on Ukara Island.

Lunch and dinner parties formed an important part of social life amongst those who had housing, wife and private transport. There was quite a social pecking-order with emphasis on seniority and long service, but I nevertheless received a lot of hospitality and, in later years, was able to return it to some of the same hosts. Private transport was essential for many reasons: bad roads, no illumination, long distances between some houses, and weather conditions such as heavy rain or excessive heat. My colleagues, 'Chuck' Rhodes-Jones and 'Mac' Mackenzie, who ran a garage in Mwanza, taught me to drive. The conditions for learning were ideal for there was little traffic on the roads. My first lessons were taken on the Mwanza airfield, which was simply a grass field maintained by a gang-mower, and large enough to receive a DC3. A popular private vehicle was the pick-up, particularly the Ford V8 thirty hundred-weight: it had very good road-clearance, was suitable for hunting parties across the plains, and could accommodate three passengers comfortably when the back of the pick-up was weighed down with a sack of sand. The landrover, with its aluminium bucket seats and rigid springs, was essentially an agricultural vehicle held responsible for the many cases of 'landrover-back' that arose among expatriates who travelled long distances over the corrugated murram road surfaces of East Africa. Most cars in Tanganyika were British-made, with many garage sales and service facilities geared towards servicing Fords and Austins. Most expatriates were Government employees and thus entitled to a car loan, usually refunded in twenty-four equal instalments. One was expected to have a British car if purchased through a government loan, and I chose an Austin A40 pick-up at a cost of 10,500 East African shillings, equivalent to £525 sterling, which was as much as I could afford.

East Africa, comprising Kenya, Tanganyika and Uganda, had a common currency, the East African shilling standing at par with the U.K. shilling, but with the difference that each E.A. shilling was subdivided into one hundred cents and not twelve pennies. Three words were widely used in the Swahili language for money, each word reflecting different historical and linguistic derivations: 'fedha' from the Arabic for silver, 'pesa' from Portuguese, who, like the Arabs, had traded extensively along the East African coast in the seventeenth and eighteenth centuries, and finally 'hela', derived from the thaler, a coin used when Tanganyika was a German colony before the first world war. Small change was often anglicised to 'changi' in the townships, but up country it was generally referred to as 'matundu', meaning 'holes', because the copper cent denominated coins had holes in the middle. This was of great practical use since extremely few African women carried purses, but could safely carry their money threaded on a string round their neck or waist, or through the end of a piece of clothing.

Our research unit had temporary accommodation on the ground floor of a small block of flats. In consultation with Peter Sewell, I converted one room into an insectary, and ordered additional entomological equipment from the UK. Colonies of mosquitoes were established, and Peter and I commenced laboratory studies on the transmission of *Bancroftial filariasis*. Much time was also given to the identification of adult and aquatic stages of local mosquitoes and beavering away at the Swahili language. Christmas passed pleasantly, with a dance at the club on Christmas Eve and a guinea fowl lunch, in lieu of turkey, at 'Chuck' and Peggy Rhodes-Jones' flat above the laboratory. On Christmas Eve, Peter Snoxall, from the 'boma', organized a short amateur theatrical performance at the club, in which I took a very minor part as a prisoner in a chain gang. New Year's Eve was also celebrated at the club with vigorous Scottish dancing, with no allowance being made for the fact that this was the hottest time of the year.

In the New Year, Colonel Laurie, who had recently purchased a second-hand motor boat for use of both filariasis and survey units, asked me if I would take it from Mwanza to Ukara Island and back to assess its petrol consumption, and take the opportunity of spending a few days on the island to see something of it and collect mosquitoes. The voyage was pure delight. There were two African crew, one of whom was mechanic and senior driver, and two of my African staff. None of us had done this journey before. We were in a lake the size of Ireland but knew that if we headed north we would see the large island of Ukerewe after some twenty miles. We first traversed Speke Gulf with its huge rocks, crocodiles and bird life, including numerous cormorants drying their wings in the sun. The boat was a sleek launch, with two 100-horsepower petrol engines, whose original use had been to ferry passengers a few hundred yards from seaplane to jetty at Kisumu. It went like a dream, easily attaining 25 knots, but we kept it at about 15 knots which seemed about its optimum speed. It was also good to be in the fresh air after the heat and humidity of Mwanza township. There was quite a mirage effect on the horizon which made it difficult to see the entrance to the Rugeye Channel between Ukerewe Island and Ukerewe mainland on the eastern side of Lake Victoria. We bore north-east and the mirage effect disappeared, revealing the channel, each side of which was lined with an elaborate series of fish traps of vertically constructed bamboo canes placed and bound close together. We exchanged greetings with the fishermen, and the children on the bank jumped up and down excitedly shouting 'puti-puti', the name given to all small engine-driven boats and derived from the 'put-put-put' sound coming from their exhausts.

On leaving the Rugeye Channel, we bore north-west, passing fishermen in their picturesque 'karua' which were canoes about fifteen feet long fitted with a lateen sail. The occupants paddled, using spear-shaped paddles, when they could not run or tack with the wind. There was no keel, so that great care had to be taken in positioning occupants and their belongings on board to maintain stability of the craft. Ukara Island came into sight, and we headed for a large bay on its eastern coast and the coastal village of Bubanja, where there was a small grass thatched hut designated as the government rest house. We arrived in the early afternoon, having covered about forty miles and used forty gallons of petrol. I had brought standard government camping equipment (i.e. green canvas ridge tent with fly sheet, verandah extension, ground sheet, canvas camp bed and folding mattress, canvas wash bowl and folding wooden stand, folding table and canvas chair) and set these up on arrival. I had barely sat down to sort out a few belongings on the table, which was sited under a tree for shade, when a large blue sykes monkey dropped onto the table and, in a flash, bit a tube of toothpaste in half, grabbed a handful of tobacco and disappeared up the tree.

Dr. Hope Trant, OBE, introduced herself some hours later. She was a marvellous old missionary doctor employed in Colonel Laurie's Medical Survey Unit. She spent several months at a time on Ukara, where she lived at Bubanja in a grass thatched hut, or 'banda', and treated Africans who came to her from all over the island. I mentioned the monkey and she replied, 'Oh that was Audrey; she can be so naughty sometimes'. I was invited to make friends with Audrey, who was called down from the tree, and I dutifully rolled her an egg and combed her fur under Dr. Trant's guidance. Audrey very occasionally bit the local people, usually women, whom she liked less than men. Dr. Trant would then be most contrite, treat the bite, and give the afflicted person several shillings. She also had a pet yellow vervet monkey called 'Puck' who once bit me on the leg through the trousers but did no harm, although the bite made a perfect semi-circular palate mark on the skin. The following morning, accompanied by Dr. Trant, I paid a courtesy call on Ntemi Mataba, the Chief of Ukara Island, presenting him with an improvised symbolic gift of an enamel beaker filled high with sugar and hoping that I said to him in Swahili, 'May your life be as this cup, ever filled with sweetness'. He was dressed in a rather grimy white kanzu and wore a grubby black felt hat and brown unlaced shoes, but he nevertheless conveyed an air of great dignity. Dr. Trant and I explained what my purpose was on the island, assuring him that it was for the good of his people, and requesting his overall support. His reply was short, dignified and conveyed through his 'mtetezi' or speaker – a common practice, particularly in circumstances such as these where Dr. Trant was clearly speaking on my behalf – 'They are pleased'. The chief was always referred to in the plural, not only out of respect but also as a reflection of his immense power. Dr. Trant and I took our departure, agreeing that the meeting had been a successful one, which I am confident was largely due to her presence.

On my second morning on Ukara, Dr. Trant appeared, as I was preparing equipment for collecting mosquitoes, and said, 'Please help me with a difficult delivery, by acting as anaesthetist: I will show you what to do'. We carried a kitchen table and chair from Dr. Trant's banda into the government rest house. She then produced a vast quantity of old newspapers, murmuring, 'Newspapers are always useful', and scattered them liberally on the table and on the ground in front of it. The young mother to be, who was from Bubanja, was placed on the table by her relatives, the husband and mother of whom were allowed to stay to watch the proceedings. She then removed the woman's clothes explaining that it was a late pregnancy and the birth might be difficult because the baby would be rather large. She asked, 'You are not married, are you, but do you have a girl friend?'. When I said 'yes', she somewhat unfathomably replied, 'Good, then you will know something about it'. She placed an improvised gauze mask over the woman's nose and mouth and handed me the chloroform bottle. I sat by the woman's head, moistened the pad, and then dispensed a few drops onto it from time to time. She lay back with her eyes closed, which I sensed had little to do with me but was in response to Dr. Trant's instructions to her. The waters broke, making a ghastly mess, and Dr. Trant became busy with a battered old kettle pouring warm water into the woman and, at the same time, telling her that everything was going very well. She then surprisingly instructed the woman and me to 'push down' as hard as we could. We both responded well and a baby boy was born with what appeared to me to have a grotesquely elongated head. Dr. Trant and mother were obviously pleased, however, so I refrained from comment. The umbilical cord was then cut and tied up with a piece of clean bandage. There was more activity with the kettle and the placenta removed, then carefully wrapped up in newspaper for safe disposal.

Afterwards, I realized that Dr. Trant, with her great understanding of the Bakara people, had simply imparted a great deal more confidence to the woman and her relations by having another 'doctor', and particularly a male one, in attendance, for a man always carried much more authority among Africans than a woman. She had also correctly judged that my role as anaesthetist would be entirely nominal and symbolic. Her care with the placenta introduced me to the importance of 'mumiani', which pervaded all aspects of rural African life (i.e. the use of human tissue for magical purposes, and the need to ensure that it did not get into the wrong hands). Mother and baby did well, with the baby's head soon returning to normal dimensions. My first name was included among the many first names of the child, and I was always well received by the villagers of Bubanja whenever I worked there.

The chief provided a guide during the next two days and I walked about the island visiting villages, noting the terrain, and collecting mosquitoes for later examination back in Mwanza. During this period, French, the District Commissioner, visited the island to hold a 'baraza' in the chief's compound at Bukiko. This was a meeting with chief and elders, generally either to receive the D.C.'s ruling on a problem brought forward by the chief, or to receive information and, if necessary, directives on administrative matters from the D.C. When necessary, the baraza would constitute a court, with the D.C. as judge giving sentence. French was an excellent D.C. He was the epitome of a Britisher in the eyes of the

Africans, being tall and slim. White men of lesser build were likely
to be asked, 'Mzungu kabila gani wewe' – what tribe of European
are you? He was like a film character of a D.C., very Oxbridge,
with the best textbook Swahili I have heard. He arrived dressed in
whites, with a white solar *topee* (hat), a gleaming launch, and
impeccably dressed crew. We met at Bubanja and he said, 'I expect
you are Smith. I heard that you had come. If you have any problems
let me know.' He was treated with great deference by the Africans
and greeted with the salutation 'Shikamoo!', which has its origins
in the old Arab slaving days, being derived from 'Shika miguu' (i.e.
'chain my legs').

Colonel Laurie showed little surprise when I informed him of the
high petrol consumption of our motor launch, but soon afterwards
it was fitted with a regulator restricting its speed to eight knots.
This was only about the same speed as the E.A. Railway and
Harbours' daily small diesel boat service between Mwanza and
Nansio, the main port and town, on the south coast of Ukerewe
Island, and infinitely more expensive. He therefore arranged for a
unit vehicle, usually our old American jeep, to be garaged next to
the D.C.'s house in Nansio, and thereafter I generally travelled to
Ukara from Manza using the diesel boat service to Nansio,
continuing by jeep to the Ukerewe Island fishing port of Bugalora
on the north-west coast, some twenty miles away, and then
catching a karua to the village of Bulongo or Bukingu on the
south-west coast of Ukara. This arrangement worked well. The
D.C. was always informed of my presence in his district, since I had
to report at his house for the official driver, and from time to time I
enjoyed the very kind hospitality of Mr. and Mrs French who
always seemed to know when I needed a good meal. The ten mile
crossing by karua was fantastic: it was better than 'Saunders of the
River', including the songs. When the wind was inadequate or in
the wrong direction, I would paddle with the four or five other
occupants, beating the shaft of the paddle on the edge of the boat in
time with the rhythm of the songs. These were very simple and
repetitive: 'Napelica majani kwa mama' – 'I'm taking grass to my
mother's place'; 'Paulo aindooket' – 'Paul is hiding in the banana
plantation' (this referred to an incident of some antiquity when
Paul committed some tribal offence and then hid in a banana

plantation). A year or so later another song, to the same tune, was added to the repertoire, 'Bwana Smithi kaa Kumsale' – 'Mr. Smith lives at Kumsale'. A favourite, widely sung throughout Tanganyika, was: 'Wadachi kazi yao ni kiboko, waingereza wamelete uhuru' – 'The German's work is the whip, the British brought freedom'. This song referred to the use of the whip against the Africans in Tanganyika when it was a German colony, and the freedom from it following British rule. I spoke to several old Africans about this and was informed that the Germans did indeed use the whip a lot.

After working from my tent in Bubanja for about a month, it became clear that, in order to get the necessary scientific data for controlling the mosquito carriers of *filariasis*, I would have to work from the centre of the island from a small laboratory, and over a period of at least a year. The chief allocated me a site at Kumsale, close to the island centre. It was uninhabited wiry grassland, with mounds of boulders and deep gorges in its red earth. Cattle were not allowed to feed on the grass which was carefully preserved exclusively for thatching the five thousand huts on the island and was cut by a special group of women called the 'wanyassa' (grass-women). There was a strong tradition of 'kazi ya msaragamba' on Ukara, whereby a large number of inhabitants would come together from all over the island to carry out work that could not be completed by a single family. It took over six months to build the Kumsale field station, which comprised four huts with mud brick walls and grass-thatched roofs, and a small outside loo. There was one large hut, twenty feet long, fifteen feet wide, and twelve feet high at the ridge, which was divided into three rooms – kitchen, laboratory, and living/bed-room – by grass mats suspended from the rafters. The other three huts were of normal size, and were for my staff of one laboratory assistant, three mosquito collectors and one cook/houseboy.

I moved my tent up to Kumsale to supervise and periodically pay the locally recruited Bakara fundis and labourers, as well as carry on with the mosquito work. The mud bricks were made, at a cost of one hundred for one shilling, by unskilled labourers using moulds from earth collected a few yards from the site of the huts. The wanyassa cut and collected the grass, selling it to me at fifteen cents for each large bundle. They were a cheerful group arriving early each morning blowing resounding blasts on a large ram's horn, and singing away while cutting and binding the grass. I located a fundi who was skilled at building with broken stones, used on the island for terracing small fields, and he built a stone foundation to the large hut. Another fundi built and thatched the roofs. There were no trees tall enough on Ukara for the main beams of the large hut, so the fundi and his men went off to Ukerewe Island and returned three weeks later grinning with success and with a retinue of porters carrying the heavy beams. He used branches of local trees for cross timbers, particularly of the raffia palm. He explained that the delay had been due to difficulty in finding a large enough karua. An adze was used for shaping the timbers, the biggest of which were held in place by strips of bark peeled from branches of local trees. The strips were first dried in the sun and then, about an hour before use, soaked in water to make them pliable. As they dried they shrank to make an extremely tight binding. Sisal twine was used extensively for tying on the thatch. The laboratory required good daylight indoors for working, and needed to be locked up when unoccupied. Accordingly, I obtained wooden planks, four times four inch timber, and metal hinges from Mwanza which the fundi constructed into window shutters and doors. I kept careful records in a note-book of work done and payments due and was constantly surprised to find that, although most workers were illiterate, they could calculate sums due to them as quickly as I could. They did this by closing the fist of the right hand and counting by lightly punching the knuckle of each finger or thumb against the chin.

The experience gained in building this field station proved of enormous value to me professionally, not only on Ukara but also in other field situations years later. I learnt to converse and even joke with the African, as opposed to merely giving simple orders and asking brief questions. I also learnt to negotiate over such matters as numbers of labourers, wages, costs of materials, and the how and when things were going to be done, and I found that verbal agreements were honoured. All the builders were local people who saw me working daily from my tent, collecting, identifying and dissecting mosquitoes, and I explained what my work on the island was about. Even long after completion of the laboratory, I was known and greeted all over the island, and permitted to engage in mosquito collections in people's houses, not only in daytime but also at night. I took the opportunity to learn most of their greetings: these were more complex and quite different from Swahili. They not only varied according to time of day, but also whether the person spoken to was male or female, old or young, married or single.

Ukara was about seven miles long by six miles wide, with intense cultivation around the coast supporting thirty villages and a total of 17,000 people, 13,000 cattle and 8,000 goats. There were also a few sheep. The villages were most picturesque, their large, grass, onion-shaped huts hidden amongst trees pollarded to provide the long shoots used in their construction. The huts were, on average, over twenty feet high and exceeded twenty feet in diameter at the base. People, cattle and goats were housed together, people in one half and the animals in the other. The people cooked at the back of the hut, slightly inside their own section, with a grass screen partially separating them from the cattle section. The cattle stood on a pit indoors filled with grass which became rich manure extensively used for crop cultivation. A fowl perch was placed about six feet above the compost pit. Cattle were rarely taken out to pasture; their fodder grass was a lush green variety grown in specially prepared hollows in the sandy shore dug below water level to irrigate it. Feeding the cattle entailed a lot of work shared by men and women. A typical day's feeding required two trips at dawn involving four miles, and repeated journeys in the evening, carrying a large basketful of grass weighing almost thirty pounds. Most loads were carried on the head, even small items such as bottles, so that the women developed a gracious erect walking posture. The heavy loads also produced tremendous development of the abdominal muscles, giving the women a tubby appearance. Cattle were generally not slaughtered except on special celebrations in a village when all would share in the feast. Cattle were wealth, the bride price being three cows. Bulls were greatly valued and very rarely a bull-fight would be held, in which bull would be pitted against bull, causing great excitement on the island and a big turnout of spectators.

The Bakara were an active, hard-working people, rarely exceeding five and a half feet in height. The old people still dressed in the skins of cattle, sheep, goat, or rock rabbits (hyrax) which inhabited the rocky outcrops on the island. The young men, dressed in worn and ragged khaki shorts, sometimes also wore a vest, but rarely a shirt. The young women usually wore a square of coloured cloth called a 'kanga': this was often worn below the waist, particularly when working in the fields, but re-arranged to cover the breasts during meal-times and in the evening. The people were proud of their tribal origins and these were the subject of much joking between them. They told me that there were peoples of three different tribal origins on the island. These were the Bakara from the west, the Baregi from the east, and the Banyangombe or Bagwe from Sukumaland at the southern side of the lake, and some differences of customs and dialect in different parts of the island reflected these various origins. At the end of the nineteenth century, the Germans united the island under one chief called Matete, who was one of the Bakara, and from then on the island was officially named Ukara. There was frequently laughter when someone referred to himself as a Mregi and the island as Liregi, which was its name before the German intervention. They told me that, although the Germans were harsh rulers, they did a great service to Tanganyika by squashing inter-tribal wars, which is why there is little tribal antagonism among the twenty or so tribes in Tanganyika these days.

I settled into daily life and work, based at Kumsale, returning to Mwanza for a few days at three- to six-month intervals to discuss my work with colleagues of the unit. I also built up valuable professional contacts outside the unit, including Dr. Margaret E. Bagster Wilson at the East African Malaria Unit in Amani, Tanganyika; Mrs E.C.C. van Someren at the Medical Research Laboratory in Nairobi, Kenya; and Mr. Peter F. Mattingly of the British Museum. All of these gave me tremendous help in mosquito identifications, particularly in the early months when I needed it most. I worked in close association with Dr. Bernard Weitz of the Lister Institute of Preventive Medicine in the U.K. to identify the extent to which different species of blood-fed mosquitoes caught on Ukara fed on human beings and on domestic and wild animals. Mr. Peter Greenway of the East African Herbarium in Nairobi identified specimens of plants which were used by some species of mosquitoes as resting places. In return, I was able to send him some information on the use of plants by the Bakara for medicinal purposes.

Hens' eggs were not eaten by Ukara women, but they were plentiful (although very small) and thirty or more could be bought for a shilling. They formed an important part of my diet, the two most common dishes being egg custard and rice pudding. A meat meal was rare but poultry was plentiful, a cockerel costing one shilling and fifty cents and a muscovy duck two to three shillings. Among wildfowl, the Nile duck or Egyptian goose, as it was sometimes called, was a common shore-line inhabitant browsing among the fields of rice and bambarra groundnuts. They were wily birds, always alert. The Bakara would trap them with nets spread out on the shore, and I would sometimes vary my diet by shooting one for the pot. My main favourite vegetable dish was boiled bambarra groundnuts, which tasted somewhat like haricot beans. Boiled or fried sweet potatoes and spinach were also part of the menu. The spinach was home grown. A large borrow pit, near the laboratory, which remained after earth had been removed for making bricks, was used as a refuse pit, the refuse being regularly covered with a layer of earth to prevent fly-breeding. Somehow, a couple of spinach seeds had been accidentally introduced into the pit. They grew into plants about five feet high and I allotted one to my staff and the other for my own use. Cooking was done on an aladdin paraffin wick stove, and drinking water boiled and filtered. The most abundant fresh fruit was the mango, which I came to enjoy. There were a few orange trees and even fewer banana plantations. There were quite a number of plantain groves, the plantains being boiled by the Bakara and eaten like potatoes.

Fish were plentiful and were regularly brought to my door, a good-sized Nile perch costing thirty cents. From time to time, I ate catfish, whose flesh was tougher and not as tasty as perch. On one occasion, two fishermen appeared bearing a lung-fish over five feet long and weighing about fifty pounds. I could hardly turn them back, since they had made such an effort to bring it, so I bought it for one shilling and my cook, Francis, put it on the kitchen table for attention later in the day. When I returned to the hut, after working in some villages, the lung fish had flattened the table with blows of its tail. I gave the fish to my staff who shared it out and clearly enjoyed eating it, although I found the small portion that I had retained rather tough and tasteless. Some of the older fishermen caught fish using a trident and they could be seen in the early mornings standing on rocks at the lake's edge with their tridents poised to strike. Most fishing was a communal activity done with nets. Twenty or thirty fishermen would walk out as far as they could go, pulling a long net behind them, and returning to shore along a semi-circular path. They would then divide into two groups and pull the net inshore by its two ends. They would all pull together, chanting 'Harambee' as each tug was made. It was customary for passers-by to lend a hand, and my staff and I did this whenever the occasion arose. Making and repairing nets was commonly carried out by the fishermen in the evenings when they sat outside their huts.

The Bakara were good agriculturalists, obtaining high yields from crops through a combination of thorough digging, regular use of manure and of nitrogenous plants, and extensive irrigation. Soil conservation methods such as tie-ridging and terracing were also used. The irrigated areas were the main breeding places of the mosquitoes that carried *filariasis*. Rice was the principal cash crop. It was grown in nurseries in January and February, the seedlings planted out in March, and large areas of irrigated rice covered many parts of the island from April to June. In April, prodigious numbers of mosquitoes bit the Bakara in their huts at night, so that some occupants would be kept awake and could be heard shouting at the mosquitoes and waving pieces of clothing about in an effort to repel them. In my own hut at this time, mosquitoes bombarded the mosquito net at night from all sides, filling the room with the humming of their wings. Some of the Bakara maintained smouldering fires near the main bed to repel mosquitoes, but this practice was quite dangerous. Babies and infants slept with their parents under rather cramped conditions and some fell out of bed onto the fire, receiving burns of varying severity. Occasionally bedding or clothing, or even the hut itself, caught fire. Burning huts went up like torches, with the hot air inside expanding so that a hut exploded at the top, throwing burning grass onto nearby huts. While the people escaped, it was sometimes too late to save the cattle. Villagers were aware of the risk of hut-fires and made long-handled rakes with wooden prongs to pull off burning pieces of thatch thrown onto their huts. In addition, in the event of a hut-fire, branches were cut off nearby trees to sweep off burning thatch.

Sweet potatoes, sorghum and bulrush millet, the last usually mixed with bambarra groundnuts, were grown between October and April in the previously irrigated areas, after harvesting of the rice from July to September. Bulrush millet and cassava, with smaller areas of sweet potatoes and bambarra groundnuts, were grown on higher land and valley slopes throughout the year. The seeds of sorghum were almost exclusively used for preparation, by the women and through fermentation, of 'pombe', which Dr. Trant informed me was a drink of great nutritional value to the Bakara, not only being rich in calories but also in vitamins. Small quantities were prepared in closely woven grass baskets, but quite often 'pombe' was prepared for ten to forty people in the traditional vessel which was a dug-out canoe. The men drank as much as they wanted and left the residue for the women. The warm liquor was drunk through a straw about three to five feet long tipped with a small metal sieve, usually made from a piece of tin can. Each drinker brought along his own straw. I was sometimes invited to take part and on such occasions took a sip out of courtesy, but found the yeasty, slightly bitter drink too warm and flat to be enjoyable. The men generally concentrated on their drinking and talked little, but sometimes there would be banter and, less frequently, overt drunkenness.

The Bakara usually came home from cultivating their fields towards dusk (i.e., at about 7 p.m.) and would sit outside their huts if it was a warm starlit or moonlit night. Sometimes there was a small fire to sit around, built of weeds that had been taken from fields during the day. The main meal of the day was prepared in the hut at about 9 p.m. and was usually eaten just inside the doorway. If the night were fine, and there was a fire outdoors, or moonlight, the meal might be taken in the open air. The principal dish was 'ugali', which was a warm, extremely heavy dough made from a mixture of bulrush millet flour and flour prepared from the root of the cassava plant. Even heavier, and less frequently taken, was 'udaga', made solely from cassava flour. The 'ugali' was prepared by scattering the flour onto a little hot water in a clay or metal container placed over a fire and stirring with a wooden spoon until the right consistency was obtained. The ball of dough was then removed from the cooking pot and placed in a wicker or metal basin for serving. There was a strict etiquette for eating ugali. It was always eaten with the right hand, which the Bakara usually referred to as the 'male' or 'clean' hand. The thumb, and preferably the first two fingers, but never the little finger, and never beyond the second joint of the fingers, would be used to take a portion of ugali about the size of a hen's egg. This portion would then be dipped in a watery, savoury relish or sauce of the day before being eaten. The relish could be made from fish (including entrails), chicken, or meat – cattle, sheep, goat, or even rock rabbit, which many of the older people regarded as a delicacy. The Bakara enjoyed a joking relationship with several tribes outside the island including the Wakerewe who laughed at them for eating rock rabbits. I found ugali almost impossible to eat because it was so glutinous that I could not generate enough saliva to swallow it. On the other hand, well-cooked rock rabbit was quite edible, although I never developed a taste for it. Quite often the ugali dish was supported by a boiled vegetable dish of wild spinach, or leaves and flowers of cultivated gourds, the mature fruits of which were hollowed out and dried to form the most widely used containers on the island.

As well as being the major ingredient of the daily main meal, cassava was the only drought crop. Once planted, its roots grew and could be dug up and eaten anytime between two and ten years, with five years the optimum. The roots were mostly sun-dried on rocks and then pounded into flour by the women, using a large wooden mortar and pestle. It was hard and tedious work which the women enlivened by singing and, from time to time, using the mortar and pestle as drum and drumstick as they sang. The raw roots were sometimes taken as a snack, a small portion being dug up and eaten on the spot. A piece of newly unearthed root a few inches long would be peeled, and the gleaming white brittle core, about an inch in diameter, would be eaten rather like a piece of celery, except that it was much harder. Pieces were offered to, and sometimes requested by, a passing traveller. My staff ate raw cassava quite easily but a small piece lasted me a long time, and even though I only accepted the less woody pieces, they took a lot of chewing. Cassava roots were occasionally eaten boiled, and much less frequently fried in slivers like chips. Cooking fat was a great luxury, a piece of fresh meat or fish being praised if it had a lot of fat or oil. It was difficult to obtain in quantity without killing an animal, but from time to time the Bakara obtained fat by inserting an extremely hot piece of metal, about the size of a knitting needle, into the tail of a live ram and draining off the melted fat. Flour from bulrush millet, the other ingredient of ugali, was obtained by removing the seeds from the cobs, either by hand or by threshing, and grinding them on a small flat, or slightly hollow, stone slab, using a grindstone often shaped like a small curling stone.

My staff and I would walk ten to twenty miles a day collecting mosquitoes. Walking these distances soon became easy and enjoyable and we would respond to the custom of accepting a little food offered to travellers at about midday. Fortunately, a frequent dish at this time of day was bambarra groundnuts. If it had been ugali, I would have responded, 'Mhavacha, lakini nimekaa' – thank you (in Kikara) but I have sat down (in Ki-swahili) – implying that I had already eaten. One of the difficulties of being an entomologist working on night-biting mosquitoes was that one required, and usually received, a great deal of help from villagers but had little to offer in return except a much repeated official statement about the expected benefits to the people that would flow in due course from one's work. Something more immediate was required and, after consulting Dr. Trant, I kept a bottle of aquaflavine solution and some cotton wool at my laboratory for treating cuts commonly received while hoeing or harvesting crops, plus a tin of chloroquine tablets and aspirins for fevers. This arrangement worked well as I treated a few people and induced many more to go to the government dispensary at Bukiko.

There was a small Catholic mission at Nyamanga, near Kumsale, having an estimated thousand converts and three-hundred school children, and a very small East African inland mission at Katende, near the south-east coast, with about forty pupils. There were also some of Islamic faith, but most Bakara were pagan and superstitious. They believed in 'wachawi' (spirits) and that some of

41

them hide inside concealed spaces. In consequence, intact vessels of any sort, notably cooking pots but also including canoes, were never left for long upside down, unless they were broken. There was widespread belief in 'mumiani', so that any human tissue was secretly disposed of. This included blood, fingernail parings, hair and faeces, which they believed could be used to exert some evil influence on the human source if falling into the hands of a witch doctor. A great deal of explanation regarding usage of mosquito material was always given to each village headman, and his permission obtained before any mosquitoes were collected, particularly blood-fed ones and at night. The colour white also exerted great power, a white goat or white bird sometimes being required by a witch doctor when particularly powerful blood was required. On one occasion a witch doctor living near Kumsale required the heart of a white egret and requested me to shoot one for him, which I reluctantly did in the interests of good relations. The Bakara women would sometimes bring their babies to touch me to bring them good luck, they said, but I was never sure whether this was the true reason.

Colonel Laurie let me use the unit's dinghy for a few weeks to study the extent of mosquito breeding offshore around Ukara Island. It was about the size of a small rowing boat but with an aluminium hull and fitted with an outboard petrol engine. The northern coast, offshore, had several sizeable mounds of boulders white with bird droppings, and which were the resting places of numerous hammercocks, cormorants, Nile duck, white egrets and lesser numbers of kavirondo crane. I had brought along my 8 mm. rifle in case of trouble with crocodile. We passed several which did not disturb us, but one looked threatening so I shot it, receiving much approval from the crew who expressed an interest in having its skin. We hoisted the dead crocodile on board and continued on our journey around the coast. Within an hour a sudden storm arose, a notorious feature of Lake Victoria, and the outboard engine stopped working. Our dinghy was thrown about like a cork on mountainous waves, missing boulders by inches. This was the moment that my crew chose to tell me that crocodiles were considered as gods by the Bakara and that by killing one I had brought bad luck. The storm blew for an hour or more and then subsided. We could not revive the engine but fortunately the dinghy had rowlocks, oars and a spare paddle so we were able to progress slowly across the rocky north coast and down the west coast until we arrived at the coastal village of Bwisya. This had a few small shops and a large hut used as a go-down for storing bags of rice prior to their shipment to Ukerewe for sale. We were tired and it was getting dark so we stayed overnight in the go-down. I was lent a storm lantern and a blanket by a shopkeeper. As the night progressed, the walls became alive with the shimmering bodies of large cockroaches. This, and the sound of rats squeaking and dropping off the beams with a 'plop', led to a fitful night.

Next morning we continued our boat journey with the aid of the outboard engine which had dried out overnight. My crew had returned to their normal cheerful selves, and one of the Mkara crew told me that many Bakara believed that when a person died the soul entered a crocodile. In the past, when a chief died he was bound by cords to a living young woman and thrown from a high rock into the lake to be devoured by crocodiles. Similarly, twins were considered unlucky and were sacrificed to crocodiles.

At sixteen years old, a man was eligible for marriage by Ukara custom and Catholic law. At this age he could also build a separate hut for himself, which was usually built in the family cluster of houses or compound. A woman was eligible at twelve years by Ukara custom, and fourteen years by Catholic law, which affected less than a quarter of the island's inhabitants. Young girls of marriageable age were sometimes called 'kipusa' because their breasts jutted forward like rhinocerous horns. All bore small tribal markings on the face achieved by filling cuts with fine ashes so that they healed leaving small, slightly raised, dark weals. Similar marks were made on the chest and upper arms of a few older people as an adornment. Some younger women made stippled patterns on their skin using mustard-coloured sap from a plant root. Working long hours outdoors made the skin dry and wrinkled, so one of the most common and appreciated cosmetics used was a vegetable oil, a small quantity of which could be purchased at a shop in Bwisya for a cent or two. The shopkeepers kept it in four-gallon drums and in two colours, red and green, but they did not stain the skin. When the skin was oiled, it shone like polished mahogany, and unmarried men would often address their girl friends as 'mafuta' (i.e. oil) in the same way that other nationalities might use the words 'sugar' or 'sweetie'. A few old men had filed, pointed teeth, which was an outdated cosmetic fashion whose origin went back to days when their ancestors were cannibals. I was told that they found human flesh rather sticky and that it could more easily be eaten with filed teeth.

The women wore necklaces of beads and also a string of beads around the waist next to the skin. In the evenings, the women would sometimes be seen piercing the white seeds of a tall, wild grass that grew in sandy locations on the island, or the black seeds obtained from canna plants which were grown near huts. These were then threaded in different combinations on thin strings made from various plant sources. Glass beads have been available in shops for over fifty years, and some of those bought many years ago had been passed on from necklace to necklace. A young man would sometimes joke with a young woman that he would like to play with her string of beads. The old men and women would smoke their pipes, filling them with hot cinders from the fire. Tobacco, called 'tumbako', was a luxury and since I smoked a pipe at that time, I was constantly asked for 'tumbako'. About once a month I would send my cook to Nansio in Ukerewe to buy paraffin for the stove and other provisions, including 'white father's cigars': these were small, triangular cigars, most of which were defective and did not draw, but I could get thirty to one-hundred for a shilling. These were much appreciated by the old people, who would shred up a cigar for use in a pipe, or grind it up to make an infusion of it in water which they would pour into a small bottle with a narrow neck. This infusion would be taken intra-nasally from time to time: the head would be tipped back and a little poured down the nose. Younger men smoked small and very strong cigarettes when they could afford it, a common brand being 'chapa kumi', a name which indicated that ten cigarettes could be bought for ten cents.

From time to time, a village would hold an 'ngoma', or dance, and this would start in the evening and generally go on all night. There would usually be two drummers, each with his own drum, and with one drum larger than the other. In the early part of the evening, the drummers would often be supported by a single string fiddle, the instrument being constructed from a dried, hollowed-out gourd with a sounding board made from the skin of a monitor lizard. The scene was most picturesque, with the oiled skin of the men and women gleaming in the firelight as they danced around a fire, set against a background of tall, onion-shaped huts.

Much of Lake Victoria was shallow and bred enormous numbers of non-biting midges. These 'lake flies' or 'sami', as they were called by the Bakara, rested on vegetation and hovered above it in extremely dense clouds. The Bakara women collected them in a grass basket through which the end of a long branch had been passed. The basket would be whirled round and round in the cloud of lake flies and from time to time the collected flies pressed down into the bottom of the basket which was shaped into a small depression. The lake flies would be removed from the basket compacted in the shape of a loaf of bread. This would be cut in slices which would be sun-dried or dried over a fire before being eaten. They looked somewhat like slices of brown bread and tasted slightly shrimpy. Lake flies and large flying ants, popularly known as 'sausage flies', were a great nuisance during mosquito studies at night, being attracted in enormous numbers to the light of a Tilley lamp. On occasions, Bakara women scooped up a few handfuls of the sausage flies, saying they were quite nice when fried. One day an enormous plague of long-horned grasshoppers descended on the island and half the island population turned out with baskets and expressing great delight. They collected huge numbers, and for the next two days the air in villages was filled with the smell of roasting grasshoppers which were threaded on thin twigs and held over a fire.

Ukara received about 62 inches of rain a year, with long rains from March to May and short rains in November and December. The long, dry season extended from the end of May to early September. This was the period of the cold, dry south-east trade winds, or 'kiangazi', which blew particularly strongly during July and August, bringing coughs and colds. Those Bakara who could afford it treated these by drinking Sloan's liniment available from the small shops in Bwisya. Another popular medicament during the 'kiangazi' was eye-lotion to treat inflamed eyes caused by sand blown into them while the Bakara were hoeing their fields. The hottest month was December, with daytime temperatures generally in the mid-eighties, but extending to 95 degrees Fahrenheit. The most uncomfortable months were November to March when humidity was high.

It was good manners to speak loudly for all to hear, a soft voice indicating that the speaker had something to hide. It was also perfectly in order for conversations to be held between speakers hundreds of yards apart where this was possible. It took me several months before I could slip easily from softly-spoken English to loudly-spoken Swahili. Good manners also decreed that one announced one's presence on arriving at a village by calling out, 'Hodi! Hodi!'. Similarly, one shouted this when visiting a hut, taking care to stand several yards from the doorway. This was not because most doors were made of grass, sorghum or raffia palm stems, and therefore would not have sounded to a knock, but because only persons of ill intent, such as thieves, would stand close to a doorway without first announcing their presence from some distance away. When a villager or hut occupant responded with the call of 'Karibu!' or 'Karibuni!', meaning 'Come near', it was then in order to approach.

Clocks and watches were virtually absent from the island, so that the most commonly used indicators of time were dawn, early morning, midday, afternoon, evening, and dusk. There was also first cock-crow and second cock-crow, which were surprisingly accurate: the former occurring at about 3 a.m. and the latter just before dawn. There was generally little need by the Bakara for more precise indicators. Sometimes, however, they referred to a specific hour in the day, simultaneously pointing to the approximate position that the sun would be in the sky at that time.

Apart from building the laboratory and housing, much of 1951 was spent on training my laboratory assistant and four mosquito collectors, making pilot studies, and then establishing a programme of work. I spent Christmas 1951 on Ukara and, in view of the occasion, had earlier sent a twelve-volt car battery over by canoe to the cotton ginnery on Ukerewe island to be charged. I also ordered a crate of beer. On Christmas day, my remaining staff and I listened to carols on the radio and enjoyed several bottles of beer and a nice fat sheep that I bought on Ukara for ten shillings.

Towards the end of the long rains in April 1951, there were lake storms that lasted over a month preventing karua crossings to Ukerewe. I ran out of anti-malaria tablets and developed my only attack of malaria in thirty years. I spent about a week in bed in the government rest house at Bubanja going through several rigours of sweating, shaking with cold and feeling very weak. My cook, Francis, fed me with chicken stew and then sat outside the door making various observations about my condition to passers-by; these varied from dying of fever to slow recovery. One day, there was much excitement outside the door with shouts about a strange thing crossing the sky. My curiosity was aroused as there had been recent articles in East African newspapers about people seeing flying saucers. However, I could only get out of bed very slowly, and even more slowly cross to the door, by which time the 'thing' had gone. I could not get a description of it but was told that it did not look like an aeroplane. When I was strong enough to travel, and the hut-building programme at Kumsale had commenced, I left one of my staff, an Mkara, on Ukara to keep an eye on the programme, and returned with the rest of my staff to Mwanza for two months to do some laboratory work and settle into temporary rented accommodation that had become available earlier in the year.

I went to Shinyanga to collect mosquitoes for breeding in the laboratory and took the opportunity to visit the long-established tsetse research station situated a few miles from the village. In contrast to the dry 'miombo' countryside* surrounding it, the station had attractive old houses and beautiful, well-watered gardens which were major sources of relaxation to the somewhat isolated officers and their wives. The well-known entomologists, Potts and Burtt, showed me something of their work and I was struck by the fact that they both, in addition to the government laboratories, maintained a room in each of their houses furnished as a laboratory, such was their interest and dedication to their work. During this visit, I was given a puppy of one of the smaller, more whippet-like ridgebacks and named her 'Jane'. A week or two later, I visited Mr. J.J. McMahon at Kisumu, from where he was

* A distinctive type of woodland.

controlling another filarial disease of man, *onchocerciasis*, in the Kavirondo valley of Kenya, sometimes called the valley of the blind because the disease attacks the eyes. He worked all hours, and in the week that I was there, my impression was that his wife was less than pleased with this level of dedication. Nevertheless, a few years later he successfully controlled the disease and was awarded the OBE. I took part in an aerial survey of Ukara Island using an adapted old Anson provided by the Colonial Insecticides Research Unit based in Arusha, Tanganyika. I met the aircraft and crew at Musoma airfield in the Lake Province. The pilot, Wing Commander 'Dusty' Miller, and co-pilot, Bill Jacques, were ex-world war II pilots, as were many pilots in Africa in those days. We flew round and across the island several times and got some useful photographs.

My temporary rented accommodation in Mwanza was one of several small buildings that had housed teachers at the newly built school at Bwiru before substantive housing was completed, and which now accommodated nearly all staff of the Filariasis Research Unit. There was a small living room and bedroom with minute bathroom en suite. I liked the standard government furniture provided, with its vernon chairs made from the heavy East African hardwoods mininga, mvule or loliondo. Included was the inevitable 'stooli ndefu' which resembled a five feet high stool and was used as a lamp stand. As there was no electricity, I used an aladdin wick lamp and a table Tilley. I bought a large Belgian carpet for the living room and had curtains and cushion covers made up by a local Indian draper. Jane cut her teeth on the carpet and a colleague, Alistair McLeod, who lived next door, would sometimes exchange cushion covers and curtains with me when he was holding a dinner or drinks party, as mine were in the McLeod tartan. There was a small outside kitchen with paraffin stove but most of my meals were prepared on a primus stove, dinner main course often being fried steak and chips, an apparently popular choice elsewhere on the campus as the evening air was usually filled with the sound of steaks being tenderized. The roof space was the home of hundreds of bats, and the ceiling of plasterboard, bulging and stained by an enormous deposit of bat droppings, eventually gave way in the bedroom during one of my long absences on Ukara. The house was

48

also infested with multimammate rats which were probably responsible for consuming most of my B.Sc. certificate, 'safely' stowed away in a tight-fitting drawer. My new Austin A.40 pickup arrived but was used little as I spent a relatively short time in Mwanza. I bought a radio that operated on a twelve-volt car battery, a portable gramophone, and well over a hundred of Sandy Milne's '78' records, which I obtained very cheaply as he had decided to go over to the newly-marketed LPs.

Most of 1952 was spent working on Ukara, where I had now established a routine programme of mosquito collecting and dissection. In addition, I became interested in filarial infections in domestic and wild animals on the island, finding quite high infections in rock rabbits and agama lizards, and Jane became quite useful for flushing out specimens. My staff, and most Bakara, abhorred contact with the saliva of dogs, but they saw Jane grow from a puppy and became accustomed to her. I found four species of snake on the island, green tree snake, Cape wolf snake, black necked cobra, and python, the latter being quite common along riverbanks, but in general snakes were not a problem. However, on one occasion I was constricted by a large python which I was holding by the neck, having shot it in the head and believing it to be dead. It had managed to obtain the necessary leverage by jamming its hard pointed tail against my right leg below the knee. Although the python is not poisonous it can inflict a nasty bite, so I had no alternative but to decapitate it with my hunting knife. Scorpions were a problem, particularly in July, when the wanyassa were liable to be stung as they plucked grass for thatching. I received a couple of stings while looking for mosquitoes resting outdoors, and Jane, stung once on the nose, ploughed a small furrow in the ground in an attempt to relieve the pain. My hut was regularly infested with multimammate rats, and Jane and I developed a most effective means of controlling them. I would throw a plimsoll, momentarily stunning the rat, and Jane would then rush in and kill it.

As well as the fabulous view from my hut looking out to Lake Victoria, the spectacular sunsets, the storms and displays of lightning, I also grew to love the noises of Ukara: the daytime chattering of rock rabbits, the call of Nile duck, and the cry of kavirondo cranes. At night, against a background of drums and the deep croaking of bullfrogs, there was the high-pitched note of tree frogs, the stridulation of giant mole crickets, and the cries of marsh mongeese and bush genet. The smell of newly wet earth after rainfall was also evocative of the island.

The Filariasis Research Unit's house-building programme was completed in 1952, and a colleague, Alan Roberts, and I were requested, as bachelors, to share a house, taking into account that I was rarely in Mwanza. The house was a typical British colonial bungalow, with red tiled roof, red concrete floors, a colonnaded verandah, and the walls inside and outside painted with cream distemper. It also had electricity, glass windows, glass panelled French doors, and an outdoor 'Tanganyika boiler' which piped hot water to taps in the bathroom. The boiler comprised a old forty-four-gallon petrol drum, mounted above a wood-burning fireplace, and periodically filled from an outside tap. During one brief visit, I was best man at the wedding in Mwanza of Joan and Ken Goatly, having worked with Ken at the London School of Hygiene and Tropical Medicine. We had a tremendous stag party at the club which affected me more than him, as I had a very low tolerance to alcohol after months of abstinence on Ukara. When I returned to Mwanza from Ukara, I usually walked the three or so miles from the port to Bwiru. Sometimes I arrived in the evening, passing Joan and Ken, sitting in comfortable, government-issue cane furniture on their verandah, and enjoying a cold drink. It was at times such as this that I mused that married status did seem to lead to improved standards of living in the Colonial Service.

In August 1952 I visited the East African Institute of Malaria and Vector-Borne Diseases in Amani, and the Colonial Insecticides Research Unit in Arusha, and then took local leave to climb Kilimanjaro. Amani, set high in the Usambara range of mountains in northern Tanganyika, was a world apart from Ukara. It was green and lush, with huge rain forest trees and extensive grounds around the unit, which in German times had been a botanical research station. It was beautifully maintained with many exotic trees. The old German houses, with their wide verandahs and extensive use of hardwoods for floor and ceiling, were most attractive and cool. I was met at Tanga by Dr. 'Mick' Gillies, in his 'safari-backed' Bedford thirty-hundredweight truck, driven uphill through the twenty-two tight bends leading to the research unit, and accommodated in the rest house or 'zoo' as it was called. Mick and his wife, Agnes, were most hospitable. Mick and I had studied together at the London School of Hygiene and Tropical Medicine, and consequently the visit provided an opportunity for lively discussions about East African mosquitoes, as well as seeing some of the field work at Muheza near by. I dined with the Director, Dr. Bagster Wilson, and his wife Margaret, who, as well as being a doctor, was also an excellent mosquito taxonomist. She congratulated me on sending her a box of nine species, from Ukara, all correctly named, and showed me specimens of species, unfamiliar to me, found in the Amani area. Bagster, as he was called, was peppery and authoritarian, but he had worked for years in the field and had a feel for his subject that commanded respect. He expressed interest in the Ukara work and mentioned that he would like to visit my laboratory there one day.

I was given a lift by private car from Amani to Arusha, a most attractive town and perceived by many as the most desirable duty station in Tanganyika. It was the principal town in the Northern Province and second only in size to the capital Dar-es-Salaam, but its situation at nearly 5,000 feet above sea level provided an enviable climate, a gardener's paradise, and, in the cool season, the spectacular scenic backdrop of snow-capped Mount Meru. The next day, Kay Hocking, officer in charge of the Colonial Insecticides Research Unit, drove me to a field station one hundred and fifty miles south of Arusha to see tsetse control trials. During much of the journey tsetse followed his car like a swarm of bees and were eventually despatched in a 'fly' post along the Babati road. The 'fly' post resembled a garage with double doors each end, and through which passed the main road. The car stopped inside it, we got out, two 'fly boys' entered the building, closed the double doors behind them, 'flitted' the car thoroughly inside and out, and then left the building for about ten minutes for the pyrethrum insecticide to act. The double doors were opened and we returned to the car and drove off. Some years later the 'fly' post was removed, a fly-free corridor having been created by clearing the bush two hundred yards each side of the road. At the field station we were met by the pilot, Wing Commander 'Dusty' Miller, the entomologist, George

51

Burnett, and the physicist, Doug Yeo. The trials went on towards dusk and we all stayed overnight in the field station, our hunger largely assuaged by a giant Cornish pasty which Doug Yeo had brought for his lunch. We returned to Arusha the following day, and early next morning I was given a lift to the Kibo hotel by Unit transport on its way to a field station in Taveta, Kenya.

The Kibo Hotel was situated about 9,000 feet up the southern slope of Kilimanjaro. The proprietors were Dr. and Mrs. Bruehl, and the hotel was a lovely old German building festooned with bougainvillea and golden shower. Dr. Bruehl had previously spent years as a missionary doctor working in the plains below Kilimanjaro and still ran a small dispensary near the hotel. In the evenings we had interesting chats about the 'old days' while enjoying a glass of cold I.P.A. in front of a blazing log fire in the lounge. He told me that many of the roads from the coast, extending well inland, had their origin in old Arab slave trails, and that there used to be a slave market at Himo where the Taveta-Moshi road is joined by the road leading up to the Kibo Hotel. The newly-purchased slaves would be used for carrying ivory and rhinoceros horn to the coast. Kilimanjaro was seen from a long distance away as a 'small shining mountain' above the clouds, its base being obscured by the heavy cloud layer, explaining its name in the trade language of Ki-swahili.

Dr. Bruehl found me a guide and two porters, and Mrs. Bruehl provided food for us all. I had brought my own Bergans rucksack and clothes, including climbing boots and sheepskin gloves, but required an alpenstock and sun goggles which Dr. Bruehl provided. On the first day of the climb, we passed through the banana grove stratum, inhabited by the Chaga tribe, and then up through the misty rain forest belt with its curtains of lichens and population of vervet, sykes and colobus monkeys. We emerged from the rain forest at about 11,000 feet and arrived at the first rest house, then referred to as the 'Kilimanjaro' rest house. It was quite a substantial building with stone walls, corrugated iron roof and heavy, wooden, shuttered windows. We stayed overnight, sleeping in bunk beds. The second day's walk was most scenic, over mountain grassland with its clumps of giant groundsel, with snow-clad Kibo shining in the crystal-clear air and looking deceptively near. We made good time and by early evening arrived at 'Peter's hut', named after Dr. Peters who worked for many years in the Kilimanjaro area in the past. There was a broken window in the small, gable-roofed rest house which, at 13,000 feet, made it pretty cold indoors. I envied the guide and porters who slept in a separate, tiny bivouac-shaped hut with minimal ventilation and a fire indoors. I drank a lot of hot tea but had little appetite, apart from eating bread heavily spread with Mrs Bruehl's home-made preserves. On the third day the porters stayed behind, and the guide and I went up 'Mawenzi', the companion peak to Kibo. We did not get to the summit but reached the top of a col very near to it. There was a splendid view of Kibo and a marvellous scree-run back down the col. We returned to overnight at Peter's hut, and on the fourth day went on to 'Kibo' hut, situated on the saddle between Kibo and Mawenzi, at an altitude of 16,000 feet. There was a piercing cold wind across the saddle, and I was very glad to be wearing my father's old leather helmet under the hood of my anorak. 'Kibo' hut was also in bad repair and the night was passed in a feeling of deep refrigeration.

The following morning we set forth at 4 a.m. by torch and lantern with the objective of reaching the summit of Kibo to see the sun rise. It was a hard and slow climb up the steep scree, but our ascent was greatly aided by the anchorage afforded by the alpenstock. Even the guide made overt recognition that the air was cold and thin, for he was now wearing socks and a khaki woollen balaclava, and had given up chain-smoking 'kali' cigarettes. We reached Gilman's point, on the crater rim, just after sunrise, but there was still a spectacular view of the red orb of the sun behind Mawenzi whose long, pointed shadow, stretched across the saddle, visibly receded as the sun rose. Behind Gilman's Point lay the outer and inner craters and the ice-stone. The guide made no mention of going on to the Kaiser Wilhelm Spitz, as the summit was then named, and I, exhausted and reflecting that perhaps climbing Mawenzi the previous day had not been such a good idea, decided that the summit would have to be attempted another time. Nevertheless, reaching Gilman's Point brought recognition in the form of a simple crown of everlasting flowers which the guide picked close to Peter's hut where we stayed overnight on the return journey before reaching Kibo Hotel the next day. The descent was sheer bliss, the ground being covered quickly with giant strides.

I stayed another week at the hotel to receive urgent dental attention at the Lutheran Mission Hospital nearby. Treatment was carried out using a wonderfully preserved, antique, pedal-operated drill. I took the opportunity to enjoy local walks and swimming in the beautifully clear mountain water at the foot of a small waterfall near the hotel. I mentioned the somewhat run-down state of the mountain huts to Dr. Bruehl and also that I had seen no other climbers. He informed me that the huts had received little attention and had been barely used since before the second world war. However, there was growing interest in the mountain, and in the next day or two a party of government surveyors were going to re-measure its height. It was apparently felt in some circles that, although Kilimanjaro was the highest mountain in Africa, its present official height of about 19,700 feet was too low, and that if it were only a few hundred feet higher it would make a lot of difference to its ranking among the highest mountains in the world. A few days afterwards, Dr. Bruehl told me that the survey had been carried out but there had been quite a bit of mountain sickness among the surveying party. Shortly afterwards, I saw the height of Kilimanjaro published as 19,340 feet, the figure that is still quoted today. Dr. Bruehl ran me into Moshi from where I travelled to Mwanza by train, breaking the long journey with an overnight stay at the Railway Hotel in Dodoma.

My staff and I returned to Ukara Island within a few days and resumed the now well-established research programme. One evening an unexpected event occurred which lost me my best mosquito collector, Lazaro. We had a very good working relationship and he had been with me through thick and thin almost since I arrived on Ukara. He was in his early twenties and had a young wife whom I had never heard raise her voice to him, but that evening they had a terrible row, in Kikara, outside their hut which was some twenty yards from mine. I went out to see what the noise was about whereupon his wife threw off all her clothes and ran to me. This action, I knew, was a customary expression of extreme distress and rarely used. I stood quite still and took no part in the incident, having seen too many badly bitten ears among Bakara who had attempted to intervene in this type of situation. I could not, however, fail to notice her beautiful shaved figure and light brown body. The next morning, Lazaro and his wife were nowhere to be seen and I never saw them again.

Two months later, Dr. Bagster Wilson arrived at Bukiko by District Commissioner's launch and visited me at Kumsale. He expressed interest in the work and results obtained but showed even greater interest in the way the buildings had been constructed, the layout of the small field station, and the organization of laboratory activities. I returned to Mwanza for the holidays of Christmas 1952 and Easter 1953, becoming increasingly aware that there was a lot more research to do before going on home leave. Irene and I wrote long letters to each other about once a month, and Irene indicated that she had booked seats for us to see the procession at the forthcoming coronation of Her Royal Highness, Queen Elizabeth in June. With hindsight, it seems ridiculous not to have taken home leave at this time, but I was then extremely busy studying the distribution of resting mosquitoes in huts, information that would have been useful in the event of a mosquito control programme. I joined in the celebrations on Ukerewe Island, organized by the District Commissioner who was now Major Batty — his predecessor, French, having been transferred to another station. Major Batty was ex-India, and, although not as fluent in Swahili as his predecessor, he was an excellent administrator. Amongst his many activities that day was taking the salute at a march past of school staff and pupils on Ukerewe Island. The school drum and pipe band played 'The British Grenadiers', followed by the National Anthem, with commendable skill. I accompanied him on the dais, he in full dress uniform, including plumed helmet and sword, and I in the best clothes that I could muster, which were a pair of well-ironed, long, khaki trousers and a clean Y.M.C.A. rugby jersey. In the evening, he placed me in charge of the fireworks display, and, as I sunk great firework holders into the banks at the lake's edge, he gave a few words of caution to the effect that at the last fireworks display on Ukerewe the operator had blown his foot off. All went well, however, the still waters of the lake providing a perfect mirror to the impressive display. Later there was a big sundowner at the D.C.'s house, attended by guests of different nationalities and walks of life, among them chiefs, officers from the health department, a district officer, a ship's captain, and prominent shop owners. The atmosphere was lightly formal and well-mannered. There was a Royal Toast and the sundowner concluded with the National Anthem.

By the end of July, I finished the studies on resting mosquitoes and returned to Mwanza to apply for home leave. This was readily granted by Colonel Laurie who went on to inform me that, on my return from leave, I would be transferred to The East African Malaria Institute as entomologist in a newly established malaria control scheme. It rather looked as if, by finding that transmission of *Bancroftial filariasis* on Ukara Island was caused by the same mosquitoes that carried malaria, I had worked myself out of a job in Mwanza and into one as a malaria entomologist.

The relative lack of supervision over me during my first tour gave me freedom to develop new methods in field entomology, but, I hasten to add, also neglect some methods that might have been usefully applied. One method then used by entomologists when studying the transmission of the yellow fever virus between mosquito, monkey and man in the forests of Uganda was to employ 'human bait'. This method had not been previously used as a routine for malaria vectors, but I adopted it on Ukara, using paid volunteers and taking an active part myself. I made collections of mosquitoes biting men indoors and outdoors at night. Dr. Baster Wilson was much taken with this technique and included it in the new malaria control scheme. It proved useful in indicating that there was some malaria transmission outdoors in the hot season when a significant proportion of the villagers slept outside their houses at night.

My innovations also extended to detailed studies of the distribution of resting mosquitoes inside huts. Bagster Wilson expressed surprise when I told him that quite a high proportion of malaria vectors, *Anopheles gambiae* and *Anopheles funestus*, rested on the undersurface of the roofs of some type of huts on Ukara, as well as on the inside walls. He mentioned that this would need to be taken into account in any malaria control scheme in East Africa, but I had no idea at that time that I would be involved in one. He encouraged me to pursue this study and write up the results, and it was for this very reason that I was late going on home leave.

It took me two trips to transfer all the furniture and equipment from the Ukara field station at Kumsale to Mwanza, including one by a diesel launch to carry the bulky items such as tables, bed and kitchen stove; and two days to say goodbye to the chief, headmen and many other Bakara that I had come to know during my period of working on the island. Some speeches were long and many ended with 'Usiende wewe Mwananchi sasa', which meant 'Do not go, you are Tanganyikan now'. While I was on leave, I left most of my belongings in the Mwanza house in the care of Alan Roberts, who also looked after my dog, Jane, and had the use of my Austin pickup. I bid goodbye to my colleagues, particularly my laboratory assistant, Mr. Francisco Balole, and the three mosquito collectors who had worked with me on Ukara throughout the tour. Towards the end of August, I caught the Dakota flight from Mwanza to Nairobi, and from there to Heathrow by the Britannia 'Whispering Giant'. As I left the customs hall, I saw Irene waving; she was wearing a little, black straw hat with half-veil, but her lovely mouth and snow-white teeth were unmistakeable.

3

Married life up country

Irene and I became engaged within a few days. I took her to the jewellers, Sacqui and Lawrence, near Piccadilly Circus, and bought a beautiful diamond and emerald engagement ring which she chose without hesitation from a selection of lovely rings. We waited in St James's Park for the ring to be shrunk to fit her slim finger, and that evening celebrated our engagement at a *tête-à-tête* dinner dance at the Strand Palace Hotel. Her parents gave an engagement party at the Trocadero and Irene looked fabulous in an emerald green dress. We went to Bournemouth for a week, staying in a small hotel. There were separate rooms and no more than kisses and cuddles, but I was just as smitten as the day I first met her, and the week went by like a dream.

Irene was a teacher at Eldon Road School, Edmonton, and gave the required term's notice before resignation. She introduced me to the headmistress, Miss Arnold, who had the highest regard for Irene as a teacher and colleague, and made it quite clear that I was an extremely fortunate young man to have Irene as my fiancee. I took lodgings in Hornsey, and during the weekdays wrote up my work on Ukara which was eventually published as eight scientific papers. During the weekends, I stayed with Irene and her parents at their home in Whetstone, and every Wednesday or Thursday evening Irene visited me bearing a picnic basket. I visited my father and stepmother in Birmingham and, while there, bought a beautiful second-hand 1936 SS Jaguar four-seater for thirty-five pounds. It had butterfly wings, enormous headlamps, canvas hood, and wire knock-on wheels. The main defect was that its sixteen horsepower engine required a new upper cylinder head gasket, generally considered unobtainable by 1953. My father, however, located one in Coventry and had it fitted by a local garage. Irene and I christened the car 'Genevieve'. We had a lot of fun with it, and Irene's school children loved it, but the car received a mixed reception on the road; comments varied from 'Look at that super car, dad' to 'That old crate should have been taken off the road years ago'!

We were married in North Finchley Congregational Church on 6th February 1954. Irene looked beautiful in her wedding dress of Valenciennes lace. She was given away by her father, and my colleague and friend in Mwanza, Peter Sewell, who was also on leave, was best man. There were about fifty guests at the reception, which was held at the Red Lion in Barnet. We honeymooned on the Isle of Wight, staying at the Farringford Hotel in Freshwater Bay. It was comfortable and warm, and we had a nice room and were well looked after, as it was apparent to all that we were on our honeymoon. The week went by like a dream with making love being every bit as good as I ever imagined it could be. Although the weather was cold, it was bright, and Irene and I spent part of each day outdoors, sometimes hiring a car or bicycles to tour the island. We stayed with Irene's parents during the following two weeks and prepared for our sea passage and married life up country in East Africa. This included buying trunks for packing the many wedding presents that we had received, and also disposing of 'Genevieve', which I most reluctantly sold to a scrap-iron merchant for seven pounds ten shillings as I had nowhere to store her. We embarked on *S.S. Warwick Castle* at London docks on 26th February, taking the west coast route. The six-week voyage was a blissful continuation of our honeymoon. For once, I did not give work a thought, being besotted with Irene and her slim, exciting body. We disembarked at Las Palmas to see the beautiful vintage cars at the portside, which were used as taxis. We climbed Jacob's Ladder on St. Helena, ate a wonderful crayfish salad in Cape Town, and visited a friend living in Uitenhage near Port Elizabeth. We had a rickshaw ride in Durban, a stroll in Dar-es-Salaam, and a tour of Zanzibar.

We disembarked at Tanga with the vessel standing off. There was a heavy sea swell and torrential rain, and we had to jump into a small dinghy alongside which rose and fell some fifteen feet or so from the foot of the ship's gangway. We went through a somewhat weather-exposed customs hall, paying quite considerable duties on our wedding gifts, and caught a taxi to the Tanga Hotel where, resembling two drowned rats, we awaited transport to the East African Malaria Institute at Amani. 'Mick' Gillies picked us up that evening and drove us straight up to the 'zoo' rest house where we arrived some three hours later ready for a good night's sleep. Irene was introduced to Amani staff 'Bagster' and Margaret Wilson, Mick and Agnes Gillies, David Clyde and his wife, Gerry and June Webb, and Jerry and Jo Shute, and we were most hospitably received in their lovely old houses. Three days later 'Bagster', as the director was generally called, sent me off to Mwanza to collect my personal effects. It took me two weeks, most of that time being spent in travel. While in Mwanza I observed, with envy, the splendid staff housing and the impressive, newly-constructed laboratory. I did not have many possessions and all went easily into my thirty-hundredweight pick-up, except a large heavy maninga cabinet that I had made locally, and which I gave to Chuck Rhodes-Jones. My houseboy, Homari, came with me as 'tunny boy' – an expression used in East Africa and derived from the days when all vehicles were started with a handle, which a 'boy' was employed to turn – as well as to mend punctures and fetch water. Homari looked after Jane when I was driving. He also had a driving licence and shared the driving. Irene remained in Amani, staying one week with Mick and Agnes and the other with Gerry and June.

In global terms, we were living in extremely promising times with regard to malaria control. Since the end of the Second world war, the new synthetic insecticides such as DDT had opened up the possibility of eradicating malaria from many countries. From 1945–1955, malaria cases in south-eastern Europe fell from 4-5 million to a few thousand. By 1949, malaria cases in Italy had been reduced by about 98%, and in the following year complete interruption of malaria transmission had been achieved in Sardinia and Cyprus. By 1954, phenomenal success on malaria control had been achieved in India and Sri Lanka, malaria had been eradicated from the USA, where it had been a problem in the southern states, and great reductions in malaria had been made in many countries in

South America. In the African region, outstanding results had been achieved on the islands of Mauritius and Madagascar, and malaria had been eliminated from large parts of northern Transvaal. It was not known, however, how the health of people would be affected by interruption of the high transmission of malaria in East Africa and elsewhere in tropical Africa, where there was a large 'immune' population. Dr. Bagster Wilson and his colleagues thus conceived the Pare-Taveta Malaria Scheme in an attempt to answer this question, as well as to determine whether hut-spraying with the synthetic insecticide, dieldrin, could arrest malaria transmission and be economically feasible for wider scale usage.

'Bagster' had recruited me as entomologist to the scheme, and Irene and I were dispatched from Amani to the Pare-Taveta area within a few days of my return from Mwanza. We drove the one hundred and fifty miles to our allotted housing in the village of Same (pronounced Sarmey), centrally situated in the experimental area. The building had been designed as quarters for two bachelors, divided by a large common room which was intended to be used as a laboratory. Each quarter had a small living room and bedroom, a separate outside bathroom with toilet, and a separate kitchen and 'Tanganyika boiler', both some ten yards away from the main building. The surroundings were scenically unattractive, the general aspect being one of semi-desert, with dusty red murram earth and boulder kopjes as the predominant features. Irene and I took over one quarter. There was standard government furniture to which we added my dog-eared Belgian carpet and my cushion covers and curtains in the McLeod tartan. We bought a few more kitchen utensils and a 2½ litre paraffin-operated refrigerator from Moshi, a hundred miles away. Homari found that the Pare area did not agree with him and returned to Mwanza, so we hired a local cook/houseboy after consulting his references which stated that he was honest and a good, plain cook. Irene was marvellous; she did not complain in any way, but set about creating a home in essentially rest house conditions. Dr Chris Draper, malariologist and officer in charge of the scheme, and his wife Katharine, also medically qualified, arrived shortly after us. They were also newly-weds. Thus all was explained. 'Bagster' had designed the quarters with the expectation that Chris and I would be bachelors during the scheme.

We spent a lot of time on safari, for the study-area was about one hundred miles long and twenty to twenty-five miles wide. The Taveta area lay just inside the Kenya border, close to Mount Kilimanjaro, and extended to the Pare area just south of the Kenya-Tanganyika border. A rest house was built in Taveta a few months after our arrival, comprising four rondavels set a few feet apart and an outside latrine. Each rondavel comprised a circular, walled hut with a thatched roof of 'makuti' (i.e. palm leaves woven to make frames about a foot square). Three rondavels were assigned as bedrooms and one was subdivided into kitchen and bathroom. They were built near the laboratory compound on ground that was extremely rocky and infested with snakes and scorpions. It was quite common to sweep scorpions out of the rest house and see snakes, usually boomslangs and, less frequently, cobra, outside the doorway. One day I returned to the rest house, after working in the field, to see Irene, with writing pad and pen clutched in her hands, running wildly from the doorway of one of the rondavels. When I caught up with her, she explained that she had been sitting in the rondavel, writing a letter, when she heard a slight 'shushing' noise, and on looking down saw an enormous snake that seemed to fill most of the room between her and the closed door. All she could think of was to escape from the snake. How she managed to bring herself to cross over the coiled snake she could not say. The snake was probably a python which had entered through a hole in the wall, made to instal piped water to a wash-basin recently fitted in the rondavel. For many months water was obtained from a local spring or nearby stand-pipe and brought to the rest house in jerry-cans. Drinking water was always boiled and filtered, with great care being taken to keep the filter candles in good condition.

Taveta was a small village and border post. There was a small, well-kept war grave commemorating soldiers who had fallen during the 1914–1918 war in a largely one-day battle between Kenyan and German East African forces on a nearby hill. The scars of old trenches could be seen and it was said that spent cartridges could still be found there. There were also a few old gravestones marking where pioneers were buried who had died of blackwater fever in times past. There was also a prisoner-of-war camp in

Taveta during the 1939–1945 war and the Italian prisoners had built a somewhat incongruous house for the District Officer in the form of a magnificent Italianate villa. On one occasion, when Irene and I were invited to dinner there, we all wound newspapers around our ankles and legs to fend off the clouds of mosquitoes. Irene, who was not an experienced cook, was introduced to a Kenyan housewife, of South African origin, who enthused over her latest culinary activity of rendering down a hippopotamus. She explained to Irene that, having made several hundredweights of biltong, there had been enough fat left over to make a great many pounds of soap. Her husband had mounted the teeth as ornaments and made cattle whips out of the hide.

Scenically, Taveta was an area of great contrasts. It was dominated by the nearby twin peaks of Kilimanjaro, with snow-capped Kibo glinting delicate salmon pink in the evening light. The climate was hot and dry and conditions most suitable for growing sisal. Extremely unattractive sisal estates thus extended throughout much of the area. The lower slopes of Kilimanjaro had a volcanic crust under which flowed melted snow-water rising towards the surface in part of Taveta area to produce a high water table and the Njoro Kubwa springs that supported a small but magnificent forest and several canals conveying water to surrounding estates. The Njoro springs were a little oasis and scenic haven, and Irene and I used to picnic there sometimes at weekends and I would swim in the deliciously cold water. Tsavo National Park was nearby, and we occasionally drove there to see the crocodiles and hippos in Mzima Springs and observe the numerous giraffe, elephants and gazelle during the journey. Some weekends we drove up to the Kibo Hotel for lunch and a break from the heat. When we could afford it, which was not very often, we indulged ourselves by staying overnight at the Kibo Hotel or the Marangu Hotel, a little lower down the mountain. We also occasionally went to the cinema in Moshi, some seventy miles away. These trips were sometimes expensive because there were heavily corrugated and boulder-strewn sections of road surface that were hard on the tyres and suspension of our small pickup. Sometimes we picnicked by nearby Lake Chala, a large, picturesque sunken lake with walls some three hundred feet high. There was a legend that there was a village at the bottom and that from time to time the sound of drums could be heard coming from below.

Within the forest lived some two thousand Wataveta who must have been some of the most studied people in East Africa. Many seldom left the forest, living on what they could grow there including plantains, bananas and gourds, eating the leaves, flowers and fruit of the latter. Many kept cattle which were fed indoors and goats which were often penned outdoors. They lived in small huts thatched with plantain and banana leaves. There was a high level of malaria transmission which received a good deal of attention by Chris Draper and myself, and also a relatively high incidence of sickle cell malaria, investigated by Tom Fletcher, who by now occupied the post of biochemist at the East African Institute of Malaria in Amani. The Wataveta were periodically studied by anthropologists because they appeared to be ethnically related to Masai, and on one occasion I saw them visited by a psychologist who had some of them looking at a television in a large vehicle fitted out like a small classroom.

To the south of Taveta Forest was a large swamp extending to Lake Jipe, the source of vast numbers of mosquitoes infesting the village of Mata situated at its edge. One day, I was driving to Mata along the road in the Girigan estate when a rhinoceros appeared from the roadside and charged towards the front of the vehicle causing alarm, not only to me, but also among the mosquito collectors sitting in the back. Fortunately, the owner, Colonel Grogan, had laid the road out straight as a die and maintained a well graded surface, allowing me to reverse at maximum speed until the rhino lost interest. I met Colonel Grogan once, near where the rhino incident had occurred. He seemed very old but was still a great walker. We had a most interesting talk about fish farming. He was a pioneer in this field and had established several ponds in the area and stocked them with Nile perch. He lived in a great house on the top of a conical hill on the estate, and was famous for having once walked from Cape Town to Cairo. The story behind this event was that the father of the girl he wished to marry would not give her away until Grogan had achieved some level of fame.

The Pare-Taveta Malaria Scheme was carried out by the E.A. Institute of Malaria in collaboration with the Colonial Insecticides

Research Unit, which made available its laboratory compound in Taveta. The buildings within it were of considerable age, and were made of planks nailed to wooden frames and raised above the ground by short pillars surrounded by ant-moats. Irene and I spent several months in Taveta soon after our arrival at Same, until I established a laboratory and field programme capable of being managed on a day to day basis by a resident field officer.

From our quarters in Same, I was able to carry out some work in the Pare area without going on safari. This pleased Irene as it gave her an opportunity to experiment in cooking with the help of the *Kenya Cookery Book*. Culinary adventures were often discarded before my return in the evenings, but cooking on a cast-iron 'Dover' firewood stove or sometimes on only a primus stove, even when performed by Alan, our cook, imposed serious limitations on one's repertoire. Further variety would be given to a meal when Alan had a lapse, such as confusing custard with white sauce. In the evenings Irene and I would sometimes play scrabble or canasta, although I usually ended up clock-watching in anticipation of what we euphemistically referred to as an 'early night'.

One of the most malarious areas lay below the South Pare mountains in the Mkomazi valley. The drive to it was a back-jolting thirty to fifty miles stretch of road south-east from Same, along the Moshi-Tanga road. Working there, based on day to day visits, was generally impracticable, so Irene and I camped at Gonja Mpirani in South Pare for several days a week over a period of about three months, so that I could examine the area properly, recruit local staff, and get a work programme under way. We had a nice green ridge tent with fly sheet, bathroom and verandah extension, and we shared a single camp bed. I found this arrangement extremely satisfactory and Irene offered no objection, possibly because at night the air was filled with noises unfamiliar to her. There were the calls of bushbabies, mongeese, and hyena in the distance, plus the occasional cough of leopard against a background of tree frogs and cicadas. Our dog, Jane, normally slept quietly near the camp bed, but one night we were woken by her excited barking. I switched on a torch to see her running round inside the tent and apparently quite deranged. There was a brief spitting noise from the bathroom extension, followed by the sounds of scrabbling against canvas as an animal left the tent. Torchlight revealed the spore of leopard where it had crawled under the canvas and stolen our supply of meat from a basket hanging in the extension. We were lucky; the leopard might have chosen Jane.

About a month after our arrival at Same, 'Bagster' came to discuss work and to break the news that Irene and I would be moving to a field station as yet to be built in Gonja Maore, near Mpirani. He usually chose Sunday for his visits, saying that he hated to interrupt us at work. He was dedicated to the success of the scheme, and, bearing in mind my field work as a bachelor on Ukara, he may have had some initial reservations as to how married status would affect my work, for he departed remarking that 'Many a good man's career has been ruined by too happy a marriage.'! Soon after his visit, we went to see the site at Gonja. It was towards the end of the long rains, when they were heaviest, and the winding path, extending some three hundred feet up the side of the South Pare mountains, was like a boulder-strewn stream. Our house was to be built on lightly forested land with heavy undergrowth, the designated plot lying a few yards above a deeply entrenched stream which was then in full spate. I pole-vaulted across, using a dead branch, disturbing a tree snake, several bedraggled ground squirrels and a troupe of vervet monkeys. The skies opened and Irene cried as we stood under sheets of rain observing the site of our first house.

In November 1954, we moved to the Gonja house which remained our home for five years. The walls were built of slabs of rock hammered off local boulders and bound with mortar, the sand for which was taken from river beds in the valley below. The roof was made of 'makuti', the floor of concrete, and the unshuttered windows of wire mosquito mesh. There was a small living room, bathroom, two bedrooms, and a kitchen with 'Dover' stove, an outdoor pit latrine and 'Tanganyika boiler'. Water, frequently the colour of coffee, was piped from a small dam built into a nearby stream. Our house was one of three similar ones, with a fourth, slightly larger one for Chris Draper who, as officer in charge, needed more space for official entertaining. The houses, one of which was occupied by Field Officer, John Hemmingway, were all built by John, using locally employed labour, including masons and carpenters. He also built the field laboratory which was situated between our house and that of the Drapers, and four rondavels as rest house accommodation.

The garden received early attention because of the prevalence of snakes and scorpions. I employed one of the local Pare tribe, Jonathan, as garden or 'shamba' boy. We worked together, leaving the few large thorn and fig trees standing but otherwise clearing an area of about half an acre around the house, using a seven-pound axe and panga. We planted a lawn of kikuyu grass, obtained from Amani, and beds of cannas, cosmos, zinnias and sweet-scented tobacco. We also grew lettuce and planted a row of pawpaw trees along the bottom of the garden. A hedge was grown along the top of the stream bank and several frangipani cuttings planted. The stream bed was straightened out, as the stream was undermining the bank, and banana plants and cannas planted at the side of the stream for binding the soil as well as for decoration. I also planted a seedling flamboyant tree which grew over fifteen feet high before we left Gonja. Snakes in the garden remained a problem, so I had a 'King Swing Slasher' sent out from a firm in Kings Lynn. This had the handle and shaft of a golf club, but ended with a curved, double razor-edged blade with which I was able to decapitate threatening snakes with a flick of the wrist. The most dangerous snakes in the area were puff adders which lay motionless, sometimes in the middle of pathways, and which could strike a passer-by. Fortunately they were rare on the site of the field station, but it was reassuring to know that Chris Draper always kept a supply of snake anti-venom in his fridge.

Indoors, Irene set to with her old Singer sewing machine, making curtains and fixed cushion covers with yards of 'Moygashel' cloth bought in Moshi. The lounge was furnished in maroon, the main bedroom in green, and the second bedroom in light blue. The old Belgian carpet went in the lounge and we bought a new green tufted carpet for the main bedroom. Some of the old McLeod tartan material was used for covering loose cushions. A storm tilley was also added to our existing lighting facility of one aladdin lamp, one table tilley and two storm lanterns. The house was periodically infested with small creatures, some harmless such as skinks and mole crickets, but others less so. Scorpions were a nuisance because they sometimes escaped attention by hiding in dark places, so we routinely inspected our shoes before wearing them and also the underside of the latrine seat before sitting on it. Once, a scorpion appeared above the rim of the bath and I hit it so hard with a slipper that it left a permanent mark, resembling a fossil, on the plaster wall. The kitchen was sometimes infested with the small multimammate rat. When this happened, Irene or the cook would inform me and, as on Ukara, Jane and I would do our party piece with the plimsoll. Once, on returning from several weeks in Taveta, we found that rats had bored through a dozen bulk-bought packets of soap flakes, spilling the contents throughout a cupboard. We became more selective about bulk-buying after this experience.

When we moved to Gonja we took on new staff, all of them Wapare – Josiah as cook, Mbazi as houseboy, and Jonathan as shamba boy. Josiah bought our meat, vegetables and fruit from the market in Gonja village at the bottom of the hill. Beef was largely sold in two categories, the more expensive one of 'meat' and the cheaper one of 'meat and bones mixed'. Many of the Wapare preferred the latter category because when the bones among the meat were well chopped up, they enjoyed eating them. The bones also contributed to a tasty relish into which they dipped their staple dish of 'ugali' which, in this area, was made from the flour of maize and white millet. The fillet of beet or 'silala' was, however, recognised as much appreciated by Europeans, and could sometimes be bought separately. Offal was not often purchased because the major blood vessels in liver were sometimes calcareous due to infection with bovine bilharzia, and brains were often spoilt by cattle hairs. We would buy ox-tail whenever possible, but demand was high and we were frequently unsuccessful. There were few sheep in the area and they were generally not brought to market, so lamb rarely featured on our menu. We ate a lot of locally bought poultry, including eggs. Cabbages were occasionally obtained from the market, but small pineapples and several varieties of mangoes and bananas were plentiful. A vegetable man came once a week from Lushoto, in the Usambara Mountains, and Kay Draper made a room available for him to set up shop. Fresh milk was bought daily from a regular village supplier who brought it in calabashes. Packaged and tinned food and non-perishable supplies were ordered by mail from a general store in Moshi which sent them by rail to Same, from where they were picked up every Thursday by one of our official vehicles.

It required a lot of firewood to keep all the 'Tanganyika boilers' on the field station supplied, so twice a week one of the scheme's trucks, along with the shamba boys, would go down the hill and into the bush only a few miles away where there was an abundance of dead wood, largely thorn bush. This lowland bush, or 'nyika', was an ornithologist's paradise, alive with parrots, hornbills, shrikes, bee-eaters and superb starlings, all of which bore the most colourful plumage. It was also full of game birds, notably helmeted guinea fowl, yellow neck and francolin partridge, and smaller numbers of vulturine guinea fowl and sandgrouse. Some evenings I would shoot a few for the pot, using the .22 rifle. The helmeted guinea fowl would gather on thorn bush branches to rest just as light fell, and for a period of about twenty minutes, before it became too dark to see, they presented perfect targets. They did, however, need to be approached quietly for they were easily disturbed by the slightest sound. There were also great numbers of baboon, vervet monkeys, ground squirrels and mongeese. Dik-dik and red duiker were quite common and these were occasionally added to our menu when the local beef, which was pretty tough, became monotonous. Cheetah were often seen, sometimes sitting by the side of the road, and rhinoceros could be heard snorting inside the thicket. Elephant were common, but rarely seen or heard for they travelled almost noiselessly at night, the only evidence of their presence being abundant spore and droppings.

About half of the population of the South Pare area lived in mountains that extended the length of the area and were separated from the Mkomazi River valley by an almost continuous escarpment a thousand feet high. During the peak of the mosquito season following my move to Gonja, accompanied by Mbazi, my houseboy, and two mosquito collectors, I traversed the top of the South Pare mountains along their length looking for mosquitoes. Mbazi and I took turns in carrying my rucksack and the mosquito collectors carried the collecting equipment. The work took a week, during which I enjoyed the most magnificent views across the Mkomazi valley towards the nearby Usambara Mountains and distant Teita Hills. The cooler mountain air was also refreshing. In the following years, I maintained regular collections of mosquitoes in huts in several mountain villages. There seemed to be little or no transmission of malaria in the mountains above the escarpment during the five years of the scheme, due to few suitable breeding places for malaria-carrying mosquitoes and too low temperatures for much transmission. The escarpment also presented a formidable natural barrier to the introduction of mosquitoes from the valley, but early stages of development of roads up the mountain did suggest that in the years ahead the escarpment might not remain so fortunate for long.

The valley was densely populated and highly malarious, vast breeding places for malaria-carrying mosquitoes being provided by natural swamps, fed from several streams and rivers descending from the mountains, and extensive irrigated areas, particularly those in which rice was grown. There was a stunning view from the valley of a waterfall on the northern escarpment. Even quite close to, the familiar noise of a waterfall was absent and for this reason it was named the 'Hingilili', or 'Silent river', by the Wapare. Many of the people lived in small, rectangular, mud-walled and reed-thatched huts, the hip-roofed huts known as 'mabanda mapaamane' (i.e. bandas with four roofs) and the gable-ended huts known as 'mabanda mgongo wa tembo' (i.e. elephant-backed bandas). Numerous cattle herds were kept and penned outdoors at night in simple, but often large, circular enclosures, the walls of which were generally made of stakes and branches of thorn bush. The extent to which mosquitoes fed on people and cattle, and where they rested afterwards, received a lot of study, sometimes involving work all through the night. As on Ukara Island, I was widely known as 'Bwana Dudu' (i.e. Insect Man) and was accepted by village inhabitants, possibly because I took great care to explain my activities to headmen and villagers and to obtain permission from householders before collecting specimens indoors. I always took part in all-night work and, on one early occasion, brought Irene with me. She was a great success, the local women and girls turning up in numbers to see a white woman for the first time. When darkness fell, the beating of drums, the flickering light from a nearby fire with its large cooking pot, and the attentive gaze of villagers, made Irene feel a little uneasy and prompted her to remark that she hoped the people would think her too thin to add to the cooking pot. I assured her that cannibalism was a thing of the past and their interest in her was purely benign. A few months later, human bones were found in a cooking pot placed under the bed of a labourer working on a sisal estate only a few villages away; this was believed to be an isolated incident.

The Wapare had their own traditional doctors, 'waganga',* who used the blood of animals for the transmutation of harmless substances into powerful and appropriate medicines. The blood of a cockerel or goat was often used, with that of a white animal being considered most potent. The vehicle of transmutation was the 'pembe ya uganga' (i.e. medicine horn) which was filled with various ingredients such as ground herbs, and then fitted with a somewhat horrific cork. This was then anointed with fresh animal blood. A ritual involving the patient followed, before the medicine was dispensed. The ritual usually took place outdoors at night against a background of a small fire and the gentle beating of a drum. One traditional doctor invited me to watch a ritual. The patient lay on the ground and the doctor briskly shook the anointed medicine horn, firstly at the patient's feet, then at his hands, and finally at his head. There was a small bell attached to the horn which repeatedly rang a dull note as the doctor made appropriate incantations. The two-foot-long medicine horn was then driven into the ground near the patient and further incantations made. It looked quite intimidating in the firelight for the cork was shaped like a head with beady eyes and filed teeth. The top four inches of the horn were covered with plaited grass rope and strips of goat skin discoloured brown by frequent anointments with blood. The horn was that of an oryx, and the mganga told me that the small bell and little ball within it were made from locally mined tin. The mganga was remarkably cordial, giving me the impression that I had pleased him in some way but I could not fathom how. He joked that a medicine horn to a mganga was like a needle (hypodermic) to a 'daktari' i.e. a medically qualified doctor). From talking with him, it became clear that the relationship between patient and mganga

* 'Waganga' is the plural form; 'mganga' is the singular.

was somewhat different from that between patient and daktari. While the latter invariably examined a patient before diagnosis and treatment, the mganga would ask the patient what it was that he or she wished to have treated. The reply might be to treat an injury or pain, but it could equally well be a non-medical problem such as removing birds from ripening crops. I showed interest in the medicine horn and, to my great surprise, he offered to sell it. He wanted to remove the bell first but I persuaded him to leave it in place. I bought the medicine horn for ten shillings and hung it on the wall in our Gonja house. It was a source of great interest to visitors. 'Bagster' said it should be in a museum and an American visitor offered to buy it. I always had to dust it myself for it was 'umwigamba' (i.e. taboo) and domestic staff would not touch it. There was a remote similarity between a medicine horn and a children's doll, and I recalled that, at the D.C.'s house on Ukerewe, someone had commented that one of their African staff had run away screaming after seeing, for the first time, a doll in a baby's pram.

There was a deep-seated fear among the Wapare of 'mumiani', or the use of human blood for magical purposes. It was not evident during daytime and indeed frequently ridiculed in the light of day. At night-time, however, suspicion was rampant and in due course fell upon the activities of our field station in Gonja. Collection of blood samples, for malariological purposes, came under suspicion from time to time. Some villagers even believed that the malaria scheme's trucks returning late in the evening from a day's work some distance away, and which could be heard grinding their way up the winding road to the field station, were carrying bodies destined for use in 'mumiani'. These suspicions were allayed through meetings with chiefs, active public relations generally, and banning our drivers from carrying unauthorized passengers. A serious, but fortunately short-lived, flare-up in suspicion occurred shortly after an injured person was found in the village just below our field station, and was thought to have lost more blood than would normally be expected from the injury. The community response of 'kupiga lukunga' was evoked, by which all Wapare, whether living in the mountains or valley, were summoned together to deal with an emergency that affected them all, such as an attack

from an enemy tribe. A Mpare told me that this had possibly not
been used for a hundred years. It was most impressive, the people
descending the mountain footpaths at night in ribbons of light
produced by each person holding a flaming torch. As they
descended they ululated, badly scaring some of the African staff on
the field station. The column passed us by and descended into the
valley. During the night there was more ululating and beating of
drums but, by the following morning, it seemed as if nothing had
happened, except that one of the larger huts in the lower Gonja
area had been broken up to pieces no larger than a matchstick. My
cook, Josiah, who lived in the Pare mountains, later explained all. It
seemed that the injured man had simply been in a local fight, but
villagers' nerves were pretty edgy and people were prepared to
jump to the worst conclusions. When, two days later, a woman
living in lower Gonja was disturbed early one night and woke up
shouting, 'Mumiani!', the age-old custom of 'kupiga lukunga' was
reactivated, and the owner's house destroyed so that evil spirits
could no longer inhabit it.

Many of the Wapare believed in the presence of good and bad
spirits. Among the good spirits were those of their ancestors who
were consulted from time to time through visits to skull caves
hidden in the mountains. An Mpare elder took me to one near our
house, inserted well inside the overhang of an enormous rock,
where there were at least half a dozen inverted clay pots containing
human skulls. More inverted clay pots, also said to contain skulls,
were almost concealed by a thick layer of clay. The elder explained
that in times past nearly all Wapare lived in the valley and kept the
skulls of their ancestors in clay pots placed or buried under their
beds. A skull would be taken out of its pot and replaced after
consultation. Terrible tribal wars drove many Wapare into the
mountains. Others stayed in the valley but hid their ancestors'
skulls in the mountains so that they could not be defiled by enemy
tribes. The bad spirits ('wachawi') lived in concealed spaces, among
the most suspect being extremely delapidated huts that have been
long vacated – analogous to haunted houses. Late one night I
returned home heavily covered in mud, including my face and hair,
after helping to push a truck out of deep mud. When my houseboy
saw me in the dim light of a torch he screamed and shook with fear

believing that I was one of the dreaded 'wachinja-chinja' who, in times past, killed people by slitting their throats. A similar revival of an old superstition occurred among the Wapare soon afterwards, when a local man turned homicidal maniac. He would appear unexpectedly in different parts of the area and kill someone, using a revolver, and then disappear. He was nicknamed 'The Cowboy' and caused so much fear that many people would not go out at night. He evaded the police for months and it was widely believed that this was because of 'maji-maji' (i.e. bullets turned to water on striking him). Eventually the police caught up with him in the nearby Usambara Mountains and shot him, but local belief was so strong that he could not be killed by bullets that his body was publicly displayed in Lushoto, and people came from far and wide to see for themselves that he was not invulnerable to them.

John Hemmingway was joined by his wife Bessie, five-year-old son Robert, and baby Diane. Robert was often on safari with his father but, when at home, received lessons from Irene. Other field officers and their wives stayed for various periods. John Huddleston sent for his fiancee who spent a fortnight with Irene while waiting for her wedding dress to arrive. I stayed in John's house during this period and was extremely pleased when the dress arrived and I had the honour of giving her away at the marriage ceremony carried out in the D.C.'s boma at Same. Jack Pearson went on leave and married Solange, a beautiful and charming Mauritian, and David Phipps drove down to Tanga airport to meet the girl he had married only a few weeks before while on leave in the U.K.

As far as practicable, I tried to keep Saturday afternoons and Sunday free of work, except for an hour or so on Sunday evenings when a little work had to be done in the field in preparation for mosquito collections next day. Sometimes Irene and I would drive the thirty miles to Same on Saturday afternoon for Irene to see the single small village shop and for me to shoot a bird or two for the pot. We would sometimes take Mbazi, our houseboy, as tunny boy. He was very strong and known locally as 'Tanganyika Jack' because he could lift the back of my small pickup off the ground when a wheel had to be changed, which was quite often, as the long thorns of acacia trees were plentiful on the road, and the tyres, when not worn thin, were perished by the heat. He would sit in the back of the truck applying 'hot-patches' to the inner-tube of the spare wheel as we went along.

Occasionally, I would get a weekend off. I would then give Irene a 'Toni perm' and we would drive the hundred miles to Moshi to do some shopping, see a film, and stay overnight in the Piccadilly Hotel. During one visit we bought a 'saucepan' radio which represented a new development in that it was light and easily portable and operated on universally available 'D' cell batteries as opposed to a cumbersome and heavy car battery. We used it a lot when we went on safari to Taveta. When returning one Sunday from another visit to Moshi, we gave a lift to four tired Wapare whom we knew well and who were pleased to sit in the back of the pickup for the remaining fifteen miles of their journey. We were travelling over forty miles an hour, which was the minimum speed required to overcome the jolting effect of corrugated roads when I ran over the tail of a very large python crossing the road. It swung up with its head, mouth open, passing over the open pickup. There were screams from the back, and Mbazi and the four Wapare leaped out of the pickup. I braked in a cloud of dust expecting to see bodies, or at least some severely wounded Wapare on the road, instead of which all five were neither hurt nor upset, being preoccupied with picking up their numerous cigarettes which had scattered across the road.

Dr. Trant was seconded from Mwanza to our scheme for several months, to assist in a nutritional survey of the Wapare, and she stayed in the rest house rondavels at the bottom of our garden, accompanied by 'Audrey'. She frequently took Irene down to her clinic to show her something of her work, and, as a public relations exercise, to introduce Irene to the people as the wife of 'Bwana Dudu'. 'Feel the spleen, big as a loaf', she would say. In response to one young Mpare woman who complained that she could not conceive, Dr. Trant told Irene to give her an aspirin. This was typical of Dr. Trant, who was immensely aware of the power of suggestion as frequently practised by the local 'waganga'. A few months later, the woman turned up smiling and pregnant, and with a gift of eggs. She introduced Irene to Audrey who rolled her an egg, but their relationship was a bit uneasy as Audrey still had a justified bad reputation for biting women. Although Audrey was usually kept on a long chain, Dr. Trant loved to give her a little freedom from time to time. One day, she entered our house through the kitchen door and, in the space of two minutes or so before leaving, had devastated the kitchen by sampling many of the food items and cleaning materials, and inspecting and rejecting most of the utensils. On another occasion when Dr. Trant gave Audrey her freedom, Irene was picking lettuce at the bottom of our garden when she saw Audrey approaching her. She screamed and John Hemmingway, who was supporting one end of a heavy beam at the top of our field laboratory, then under construction, let go and ran to her aid by scaring off the monkey. He then returned to the beam where his assistant had been giving a good performance as 'Atlas'.

Irene and I spent our first Christmas at home having guinea fowl for dinner instead of the traditional turkey. Our Christmas tree was a large branch of thorn bush, with the thorns removed, and decorated with balloons and bows of coloured paper. Irene made up small presents for our colleagues and we gave each of our house staff cash, sugar, dried fruit and a bottle of beer. Chris and Kay Draper laid on a most hospitable New Year's Eve party.

In the following year, I was heavily occupied with field work and the time sped by, punctuated by occasional Sunday visits by 'Bagster'. Irene had a miscarriage early in the year when she was about three months pregnant. Chris and Kay were on safari at that time, but Sister Erica came down from the Lutheran Mission Hospital at Bombo in the Pare Mountains and looked after her. Shortly afterwards, I accompanied Irene up to Moshi, for a D and C, in one of our official vehicles, a thirty-hundredweight Bedford truck. We met 'Bagster' driving down with Sir Bruce Hutt, the East African High Commissioner. We both stopped and 'Bagster' conveyed his condolences, mentioning that he had had the same experience with his wife. He departed, expressing the hope that I would be back in Gonja in time for a meeting that evening. Irene quickly recovered and we continued to drive up and down the corrugated roads of the Taveta-Pare area, but taking a little more care with deep depressions in the road.

Work continued unabated until Christmas 1955 which we spent in Arusha with our friends, Ray and Peggy Foster. December was generally a hot and humid month, but the Arusha air was much cooler than in Gonja and made a welcome change. We also enjoyed the few days of civilized environment provided by the Arusha home of the Fosters and the New Arusha Hotel. In company with the Fosters, we attended a Christmas Eve dance at the 'Beehive' and a New Year's Eve dance at the Arusha Gymkhana Club. Arusha was very much a senior station and the club atmosphere initially felt a little overpowering, being dominated by the conversation of senior colonial officers. I also felt a little strange in evening dress, although Irene looked as attractive as ever, even though she was six months pregnant and bore my 'Toni' perm. Nevertheless we soon got into the swing of things as the evening progressed.

A fortnight before the baby was due, Irene and I went up to Taveta area, which was some eighty miles nearer to Moshi than Gonja. I worked on mosquitoes in Taveta Forest and Irene knitted baby clothes. Contractions began one Thursday and I drove Irene up to Moshi hospital where she was admitted by Dr Hurd who had earlier carried out the D and C. She was given a small ward to herself, shared on Friday night by the Sister-in-Charge. On Saturday morning I mooned around the hospital, and Dr. Hurd suggested that I went to the cinema in the afternoon where I could easily be located if necessary. Irene gave birth to a healthy daughter early in the afternoon of Saturday 10 March 1956, and Dr. Hurd came round to the cinema with the news. After the birth, Irene spent a fortnight in the hospital as the delivery had been slightly traumatic. I returned to Taveta and visited her two or three times. When considering a name for our daughter, we oscillated between 'Linda' and 'Susan', but the former won as Linda, as well as being a popular name at the time, particularly in America, was also Swahili for 'guard' or 'look after'. The return to Gonja was quite eventful. We rounded one corner and skidded into a ditch to avoid hitting an elephant in the road, and shortly afterwards turned another corner only to hit a large boulder in the middle of the road that had possibly been dislodged there by passing elephant. The sump shield was inadequate and the impact dismounted the engine, driving the connecting rods through the bottom of the sump. A car eventually came by and conveyed Irene and baby, both covered in a heavy coat of red latterite dust, to a less than triumphant return to Gonja. I stayed behind to await an official vehicle to tow me home.

Linda went from strength to strength after losing weight for the first week. For the first few months she slept in a woven grass basket lined with cloth and placed on a refrigerator box to protect her from scorpions and ants. She was also kept under a mosquito net at night and, when a few months old, given a quarter of a tablet of paludrine a day as malaria prophylactic. Fortunately, there was no malaria drug resistance up country and Linda never developed malaria. Nor indeed, did Irene and I who took one 25 mg. paludrine tablet a day throughout our married life in East Africa.

When Linda was about five months old, we bought a collapsable pram with carry-cot and Irene would often wheel her to the bottom of the garden where there was a shady spot created by the pawpaw trees. One day, I was in the outside toilet when I heard a scream from Irene. I rushed out to seen an enormous baboon descending a giant fig tree, situated next to the pawpaw trees, with its eyes concentrated on Linda asleep in the pram. My old mauser rifle earned its keep that day. I ran into the house, loaded it and, leaning against the wall of the latrine, shot the baboon through the heart. It fell into a fork in the tree whereupon our rather small houseboy, Hamisi, scrambled up a long branch that reached close to the ground. Irene, distraught and not recognizing Hamisi, who was largely concealed by the dense foliage of the tree, shouted 'There's another one!'. I swung my rifle round until the sights were on the moving target, but recognized Hamisi in good time. Hamisi pushed the baboon free of the fork, and I took a photograph of Irene and Hamisi standing each side of the baboon. The baboon was very heavy, but Hamisi and I dragged it to a nearby cliff and pushed it over the edge. For the following three nights we heard the cough of a leopard nearby and each morning saw that it had fed on the body of the baboon.

A day or two later, Irene and I were having dinner when there was an almighty clang outside the kitchen door of the Hemmingway's house. I ran out into the dark with my rifle and, on hearing a noise in the undergrowth, came face to face with Bessie Hemmingway also bearing a rifle, since John was away on safari at that time. The intruder turned out to be the leopard, which had now stopped feeding on the baboon, had entered the kitchen, seized the Hemmingway's alsatian dog, and, springing out of the doorway, had landed on a metal wheelbarrow, knocking it over. It released the dog, which was found to have four deep holes in its neck where the leopard had buried its canine teeth. The vet at Same filled the holes with penicillin powder and it took three months for the dog to recover fully from its ordeal.

During 1966, Princess Margaret visited Tanganyika and I attended a rally which she addressed at Tanga. It was an impressive event with bands playing, tribal dances and speeches; and I was happy to see Princess Margaret, whom I had always admired. One evening, a week later, I was doing some heavy gardening in vest and shorts, when a man appeared saying that his vehicle had broken down and asking if he could stay overnight. Chris and Kay were on safari, so Irene prepared a bed in one of the rondavels and invited him to dinner. To our surprise he came to dinner wearing a vest and no shirt. I think this was his idea of fitting in. He gave the appearance of never having left the Home Countries and was amazed at everything around him. Next morning he produced a sophisticated movie camera and extensively photographed our family, house, garden and other aspects of the field station. He explained that he was one of the advance party for Princess Margaret who was going from Tanga to Arusha to open a school. His duties involved photography and matters of detail, including fitting a new toilet seat and approved type of paper. His car was found to be very low on water and in need of more engine oil and, when this was remedied, it started without further trouble.

When sufficient information on malaria and its transmission had been obtained, and the position of the huts in the area mapped, the huts were sprayed with insecticide, the first application being completed in November 1955. The Wapare and Wataveta were delighted. They were no longer pestered by mosquitoes in their huts and, even more pleasing to them, the insecticide also proved extremely effective in controlling bed bugs. A second application was completed by August 1956 with equally impressive results. By this time, the World Health Organization had set as its objective world eradication of malaria in ten years, with possible exception of parts of Africa. The findings, methods and techniques used in the Pare-Taveta scheme came to its attention, with the consequence that we had numerous visitors of many nationalities, including entomologists, malariologists, administrators and people in charge of large insecticide spraying programmes. Many came carrying sophisticated cameras and dressed in bright shirts and blue jeans in contrast to my typical colonial field dress of khaki shirt and shorts. As individuals they were pleasant and attentive, and I made great efforts to show and explain my work, but it was sometimes hard going as many did not speak English well enough to understand much detail. Nevertheless, nearly all left expressing thanks and saying that they had benefited from their visit.

I was well into the sixth year of my career before I took any interest in my financial position, except not to spend more than was in my bank account. 'Bagster' once advised me to 'leave administration to the administrators' and I was very happy to do so. After Linda's birth, I was once again rather strapped for cash because of a sizeable backpayment I had made when given the opportunity to join the Overseas Superannuation Scheme retrospectively. Then, one day, I accidentally came across an old salary slip that had escaped the usual fate of being thrown away after being received. It showed a deduction of income tax had been made that month which was in a year that I thought I had paid my income tax by cheque. I took this up with the Income Tax Department in Dar-es-Salaam and received a refund. Life was never quite the same after this. I kept all salary slips and never left administration entirely to the administrators.

In November 1956, about halfway through the scheme, I went on home leave. We first travelled down to Amani Headquarters and stayed two days in the boma with the Acting Director, Dr. McLean and his wife, as 'Bagster' and his wife were on home leave. We embarked on *S.S. Rhodesia Castle* at Tanga and, because of the prevailing Suez crisis, had to take the west coast route, also entering the Mediterranean Sea to pick up passengers from Gibraltar, Genoa and Malta. The voyage took six weeks and was very pleasant except for a terrible storm near the Golfe du Lion in the Mediterranean Sea. The ship seemed to toss through almost 180 degrees. Irene was seasick and confined to her bunk which was fitted with a net to stop her being thrown out. The cabin was flooded to a depth of over a foot, and water entered baggage, damaging belongings, including our marriage certificate. Linda survived a week with me bottle-feeding her, using the 'Milton method' applied under somewhat acrobatic conditions. We stayed with Irene's parents in London who were completely captivated by Linda. With funding obtained through the usual government car loan, repaid through twenty-four equal instalments, I bought a new car under the 'home-leave plan' (i.e. free of U.K. tax, but liable to import duty on entering Tanganyika). I obtained a temporary U.K. driving licence against my Tanganyikan one and we drove down to Torquay for a week, hardly meeting anyone on the road as petrol was severely rationed except for overseas visitors. Irene's brother and I went to Switzerland in February and spent a fortnight skiing in Andermatt. In March, Linda was christened in the church in which Irene and I were married and, a few days later, we embarked on *S.S. Kenya* at London docks for the return journey to Tanga, again by the west coast route as the Suez crisis was still on. The voyage was pleasant enough and Irene and I won a prize as the 'Hobo-twins' in the fancy dress contest. We disembarked at Tanga and drove up to Gonja in our new car with the largest item of baggage, an enormous box of paddi-pads, tied onto the roof rack.

There was much to do on returning to Gonja, not only in the field, but also in writing up results obtained during the previous three years. The insecticidal treatment of huts in the malarious area dramatically reduced malaria transmission, with the malaria-carrying mosquitoes remaining susceptible to the insecticide at all times, and one species, *Anopheles funestus*, was apparently eradicated. Bouts of 'homa' or malaria fever became things of the past and, in general, the malaria scheme was greatly appreciated by the inhabitants to the extent that people living outside the area asked to be included in it. However, all was not plain sailing. Shortly after the first application of insecticide, there was an outbreak of 'utitiri', or chicken mites, which, although not biting people, infested them in such numbers as to cause itching of the skin and a humming or tickling sensation in the ears. Later on, bed-bugs, fleas and certain house-frequenting mosquitoes became resistant to the insecticide and proliferated to become serious pests. The inhabitants thought that this was because we had changed from using 'dawa kali' to 'dawa dhaifu' (i.e. from strong to weak insecticide). Much explaining was required to convince them that this was not the case. While collecting bed bugs and fleas from the beds of villagers for tests, I sometimes inadvertently acquired one or two on my clothing and brought them indoors. Irene, of course, was not amused, and even less so when I would not allow residual insecticides to be used in our house because of fear of contaminating insect colonies in the field laboratory.

In September 1957 we arranged to spend a weekend in Lushoto to enjoy the cool air of the Usambara mountains. Travelling in the new car was infinitely more comfortable then in the old pickup and Linda was now old enough to be carried on Irene's lap. As we rounded a corner, we were struck by an oncoming bus travelling on the wrong side of the road. Linda shot off Irene's lap and landed on the floor of the car in a cloud of red dust. Irene hit her head on the windshield, shattering the glass, and the door of the glove compartment sprang open, deeply gashing her leg. After ascertaining that Linda was unhurt and tying up Irene's injury with a clean handkerchief, I jumped out of the car to be confronted with a beaming driver who had been sacked from our scheme only a few months earlier for dangerous driving. Even in these circumstances, when an expletive would seem to have been in order, the essential good etiquette demanded of Swahili greetings was so deeply ingrained that we greeted each other warmly and stated that we were well, but 'my wife was injured and my new car badly damaged'. With the help of several passengers, we raised the mudguards free of the front wheels and I drove to Korogwe police station to report the accident and then on to Tanga hospital where Irene was stitched up. Before returning to Gonja, we stayed in the Tanga hotel for a few days for Irene to recover and for the car to be made roadworthy.

In the months that followed, until the end of the scheme, even the weekends were taken up mostly with work, as investigations deepened to find the reason for the continuation of an albeit extremely low level of malaria transmission in the treated area. More detailed studies were made on the behaviour of the malaria carrying mosquitoes and of villagers' habits, until a combination of factors was eventually distinguished which offered an explanation. Three of these were that the malaria mosquito spent some time feeding and resting outdoors; in the hot weather, about a fifth of the people in some parts of the treated area, slept outdoors; and enclaves of new huts were being built and inhabited between cycles of spraying.

As much time was spent based at Gonja, on-site recreation was provided by Chris Draper, who had a badminton court built early in the scheme and a small concrete-lined swimming pool constructed three years later. Playing badminton at Gonja was an enjoyable but unique experience. While the site of the court provided a magnificent view towards the Usambara mountains, the strong thermal air currents rushing up from the Mkomazi valley in the evening made it difficult to align the racket with the shuttlecock. This problem was, however, overcome by inserting a judicial amount of plasticine inside the cone of the shuttlecock. The pool, about twenty feet by ten, was periodically filled with stream water which, being loaded with mica-schist, was the colour of coffee. Nevertheless it provided a much appreciated cool dip, and Linda and Kay Draper's daughter, Philippa, who was a few months younger than Linda, both enjoyed being pushed about on lilos.

We spent Christmas 1957 in Lushoto, staying at the Lushoto Hotel visiting 'World's End' and enjoying walks in the cool air. An interesting walk was across an old golf course which had not been used for years and had gone to bush, although most tees and greens were still discernible. It was said that the course had been privately built by an old colonial who had retired to Lushoto and had greens and tees constructed to resemble those on various famous golf courses throughout the world. Irene mentioned that she might be pregnant again. This was welcome news as we had planned to have two children fairly close together, and both before the end of the malaria scheme.

Towards the end of May, Irene's friend, Hilda Griggs, came out from England to spend three weeks on holiday with us in Gonja, and on the Saturday following her arrival our neighbour Barbara Butler held a small party which included a little dancing. When we returned to our house, Irene discovered that she had a haemorrhage. Next day I drove Irene up to Moshi hospital where she remained for ten days and was advised to continue her pregnancy within each reach of a hospital. Kay Hocking made available a temporarily vacant house in Arusha, provided with hard furnishings. Irene and Linda stayed in the Arusha house, and were looked after by our faithful cook, Josiah, and I stayed in the rest house rondavels in Taveta, returning to Arusha for the weekends. My work unexpectedly benefited from this change as I was able to give more time to studying a malariologically important group of mosquitoes inhabiting Taveta Forest. Hilda was invited to Amani where she had a very pleasant time as the guest of Mick Gillies and his wife Agnes. Irene gave birth, in the Arusha hospital, to a healthy baby girl on Saturday, 26th July 1958, and a few days later we returned to our Gonja home. We named the baby Diana, in honour of the goddess of the chase.

Following Diana's arrival, we had a small mud and wattle room built as an annex close to our Gonja house to serve as a dining room and allow space in the living room for a play pen. (Play pens could only be placed outdoors when someone was present to guard against snakes and scorpions.) We were also strapped for funds, because of Irene's confinement in Arusha, but she saved the day by cashing in her teacher's pension. For the same reason, we stayed at Gonja for Christmas 1958, and on New Year's Eve, Kay Draper held a splendid party attended by Dr. Jerry Pringle who was due to take over as Director of the East African Institute of Malaria at the end of the scheme in May 1959, coinciding with Bagster's retirement.

With only a few months to go before the end of the scheme and going on home leave, there was much to do. A start was made on drafting scientific papers and contributions to the final report of the scheme. Irene placed an advertisement in *The Lady* for home leave accommodation and we had about seventy replies from all over the U.K. We thought that it might be nice for our children, as well as ourselves, to spend the summer months by the seaside. Accordingly, we accepted an offer of full board in a private house situated very close to East Wittering beach in Sussex. I was concerned about future employment and was offered research work on *filariasis* based on a field station in a forest in Ghana. However, I was reluctant to accept another up-country post, as I wanted Irene and our children to live in a house with electric light and clean running water. Besides, Linda, who was three years old, needed more companionship of English-speaking children of her own age and to grow up in a more typical European way; the time had come for her to stop looking with daddy for 'jong-jongo' under stones and sucking baobab seeds as 'sweeties'. Salvation came in an unexpected way. Each year, usually in January or February, a group of three senior representatives of the British Medical Research Council and the Colonial Office visited Gonja to assess the progress of the scheme. They usually comprised Sir Gordon Cavell, Professor P.C.C. Garnham, and Dr Lewthwaite, and we collectively referred to them as 'the old men'.

All these 'old men' were given great respect for they themselves had spent many years working under difficult field conditions and had made notable contributions to tropical medicine. They were welcome visitors for, although a little overwhelming, they made valuable comments in technical discussions, and showed genuine empathy with people working in the field. During their last visit, before the end of the scheme, Linda noticed them coming round to the laboratory and shouted, 'Here come the old men'. As usual, I disgorged a whole lot of my research findings at them, which were almost invariably received with a studied air of tranquillity since they had probably, and quite rightly, already heard about them a little earlier from Chris Draper as Officer-in-Charge of the scheme. Professor Garnham was interested in monkey malaria, so we went down to Mpirani forest where I shot him a sykes and a vervet monkey, both of which he dissected in the laboratory, finding one with an overt malaria infection of the liver. Dr. Lewthwaite, after listening to my scientific babble for ten minutes or so, came over to our house and (as usual) spent half an hour or more talking football with Irene whose father was a staunch supporter of Arsenal, and who had imparted a formidable knowledge of players and teams to his daughter. Their conversation was concluded with Dr. Lewthwaite asking Irene where she would like to be stationed next. She unhesitatingly replied 'Arusha' and Dr. Lewthwaite left, remarking, 'And so you shall, my dear'.

Photogaphers and information officers of the East African High Commission descended on Gonja. Many photographs of excellent quality were taken of the Drapers and Smiths in the field, laboratory and at home. Copious notes were also made and, in July

85

1959, local newspapers carried extensive and illustrated accounts of the scheme. The *East African Standard* carried a large article headed 'Five-Year Experiment Shows The Way To Defeat Of Malaria', and the *Tanganyika Standard* 'Two Men on a Mountain Beat Malaria'. The articles indicated that the experiment had cost £136,000, comprising £69,000 from colonial development and welfare funds, £57,000 from East African governments, and £10,000 worth of insecticide provided by the United Nations Children's Fund (UNICEF). The magazine *Commonwealth Today*, prepared by the Central Office of Information, London, published a well-illustrated article headed 'Science v. Malarial Mosquitoes – Successful Five-Year Campaign in East Africa'. Two months later, the *Birmingham Mail* published a picture of Irene and me with our two children in our garden in Gonja, alongside an article headed 'The doctor's lonely battle in the wilds of Africa'.

Dr. Bagster Wilson, who was responsible for getting the experiment under way and picking the spot for it, did not live to enjoy its success for he died of a heart attack while on retirement leave.

In late May 1959, Irene and I packed up our few possessions in empty insecticide drums, which were then loaded on a truck and taken to Arusha where they were placed in store at the Colonial Insecticides Research Unit (CIRU). We thanked our colleagues and many local Wapare for their help and kindness. While we had experienced local problems, particularly with 'mumiani', there had been no national ones. The green and black flag of the Tanganyika African National Union (TANU) was visible in several villages and there had been a national election in which Mheshimiwa Julius Nyerere had been elected 'kiongozi', or leader, of TANU to lead the country to independence by peaceful means. We were also fortunate in that, in our isolation, we had not been aware of the new drug, thalidomide, for treating sickness in pregnancy. We drove up to Arusha in our own car, storing it at CIRU and staying overnight in the New Arusha Hotel, before proceeding on home leave the following day.

We travelled to Nairobi in a rickety old public bus filled with Africans of many tribes, chickens, goats, and hazardous lengths of sugar cane, which were fortunately eaten down as the journey progressed. Linda and Diana were a great hit with the African women who touched them and showed great interest in the way they were dressed. We flew from Nairobi in a Britannia aircraft, arriving at Heathrow where Irene emerged with her short dress contrasting with the ankle-length dresses all around her that were characteristic of the prevailing fashion. We hired a chauffeur-driven car to take us to 'Roshanara' in East Wittering, where we spent five glorious months during one of the longest and hottest summers for years. We enjoyed long days on the beach with the children, and most evenings watched TV, which was a new experience for us. We were visited by friends and relations, had Diana baptised in the local Congregational Church, and I went on a dinghy-sailing course held at nearby Itchenor. I also bought a set of old hickories, mostly Hogans, in an old leather bag for £1, for practising golf swings on the beach. Irene and I even managed to attend a few local dances through the kindness of our hostess and her daughter who babysat on those occasions. We returned to Arusha by air, after a long delay at Heathrow involving a re-landing with a six-hour delay, requiring us to borrow back Diana's folding pushchair which we had previously given to a ground hostess. We had a bumpy flight from Nairobi to Arusha in old Dakota, but were glad to be back in East Africa and especially to be stationed in the beautiful town of Arusha.

4

Arusha

We spent thirteen years in Arusha, all of them happy and interesting, and several of them quite eventful. I was allocated a bungalow in an acre of neglected garden, for the house had been unoccupied for many months. It was one of the least envied houses in the housing pool because it was situated near undeveloped land where landfill activities had been carried out in the recent past. Irene and I thought it was wonderful. The bungalow had been built by colonial development and welfare funds in about 1950. The lounge was a good size, with two windows to the back and to the front, and French windows opening onto a covered veranda supported by twin pillars. There was a fireplace in the lounge and, in the coldest month of July, we would bask in the warmth of log fires in the evenings. The lounge opened into the dining room through double doors. There was a small pantry and large kitchen fitted with a cast-iron wood-burning 'Dover' stove. There was clean piped water, the hot water coming from a wood-burning 'Tanganyika boiler' fitted at the back of the house. There were two bedrooms and a small room which was usually used as a box-room, but which occasionally functioned as a third bedroom. In addition to the bathroom, there was a separate flush-operated toilet. It took me several weeks to get out of the habit of checking the toilet seat for scorpions after nine years of using outside loos. The walls were brick built and plaster rendered, and all painted in cream distemper inside and out in conformity with usual government practice. The roof was fitted with red tiles, and all floors were highly polished with 'Cardinal Red'.

The garden sloped down from the house on all sides, offering a spectacular view from the veranda, in the cool season, of clouds of beautiful blue flowers on the jacaranda trees which bordered the garden, and, beyond them but seemingly quite near, snow-capped Mount Meru rising to 14,979 feet. In December, in the hot season, the long drive from the road to the house was aflame with red flowers of the flamboyant trees which lined it, and the road itself colourful with the red blossom of tulip trees planted along its edges. The house had previously been the home of a botanist and keen gardener, Giles Ivens, so that the garden, although knee-deep in thistles and other weeds, contained a variety of flowering plants and shrubs. We engaged a gardener or 'shamba boy', bought gardening tools such as hoes, slashers and a 'Kikuyu' lawnmower, and within a year had a most beautiful garden. There were red and orange bougainvilleas, a glorious oleander that filled the garden with its scent in May, several pride of India, prolifically flowering red, white and yellow frangipanis, poinsettias, hibiscus, sweet-scented and yellow jasmine plants, and large rosebeds of hybrid teas and floribundas. Close to the house was a well stocked rockery, and bordering it agapanthus and dahlias. Beautiful blue petreas climbed each side of the veranda, which had a low wall with troughs planted with profusely flowering ground orchids. We planted a conifer hedge around the garden, and, a year or two later, an acacia tree, planted at the bottom of the garden, came into bloom to give a dazzling display of yellow flowers.

Irene made a lovely home of 169, Hellenic Road in our early years in Arusha. Hard government furnishings were provided, but our soft furnishings, brought up from Gonja, were mostly too 'bush' and had to be discarded. A few items, such as cooking utensils, were retained, including the kerosine refrigerator and an old wooden box that Josiah insisted on retaining as his kitchen seat. The Indian carved 'elephant' table and occasional tables that had survived my Mwanza days were placed in the lounge. British furnishing materials, once so prominent in Tanganyika, were becoming replaced by those from other countries as there were difficulties in achieving delivery dates with some British goods. We were, however, able to obtain a new Wilton carpet for the lounge, as the two carpets from Gonja had a nasty reddish tinge imparted by the red latterite dust that pervaded most materials there after a year or two. Irene bought British curtain material, and jinja cotton cloth for covering cushions, from Zaverchand's shop in Arusha, and had them made up. Over a period of years, we added a few interesting items of Africana, such as a bow and poisoned arrows in its holster, throwing spears and shield from Umbugwe, drinking cups from Taveta forest, knobkerries from Masai, a medicine horn from Upare, and an *ibeji* and head mask from Nigeria. Paintings by local artists and sporting prints, bought on home leave, were hung in the lounge and dining room, and a nice clock, purchased from Garrards in Regent Street, was placed on the mantelpiece. We bought a mains operated valve radio and Telefunken record player from a friend returning to live in the UK. Irene had her old upright piano shipped out from home. It arrived in pieces, the sides split and the hammers broken and apparently beyond repair, but Dick Rapley, a neighbour and officer in charge of the CIRU workship, felt it a challenge to repair it. Within a few weeks he delivered it to us in perfect playing condition.

The Colonial Insecticides Research Unit was a large Tanganyika government research station situated seven miles from Arusha. Its activities centred on the development of ways to control mosquitoes, tsetse flies, species of aquatic snails that transmit bilharzia, and the many pests and diseases of major crops such as coffee, cotton, sugar cane and maize. There was a staff of about one hundred and thirty, including the Officer-in-Charge, seven entomologists, two botanists and two chemists, and one plant pathologist, malacologist and physicist. I was recruited to assist the unit in the development of new insecticides for control of mosquitoes, since malaria campaigns in several parts of the world were threatened by the appearance in malaria-carrying mosquitoes of resistance to DDT and related insecticides. In early 1960, the World Health Organization developed a programme for evaluation of new insecticides for malaria control. There were six stages: the first three carried out within laboratories; the fourth comprising field trials in malaria mosquito infested areas, using specially constructed 'experimental' huts; the fifth being trials in which huts or houses in a few villages were treated; and the sixth comprising large-scale trials involving malariological as well as entomological assessments. Stage IV was assigned to the CIRU which was accordingly designated a 'World Health Organization collaborating laboratory'.

Kay Hocking put me in charge of the Stage IV trials which I recognized would be vitally important for the success of many future malaria control operations. However, I also thought they would be entirely routine, rather boring, and do very little for my professional career. I was wrong on all counts. The two areas in which the trials were carried out were extremely interesting. The main area, Magugu, situated about ninety miles south of Arusha, was next to Lake Manyara at the foot of the rift wall and close to the justifiably famous Manyara game reserve abounding in buffalo, elephant and lion, and with a spectacular avifauna which included flamingos, pelicans and storks. The other area was near Taveta forest which I knew quite well. I developed an interest in the effects of insecticides on mosquito behaviour and was able to supplement the more routine experimental hut work with innovative studies involving new designs of experimental huts and two new field laboratories. The local people made land available for these studies when I promised and made a deep well, for their use, close to each of two new experimental hut sites at Magugu and Taveta. I had long learned that influential villagers were often cynical of promises of benefits to be gained in the distant future. I was also able to continue observations on transmission of malaria in the Taveta area that I had started at the beginning of the Pare-Taveta scheme in 1954, and so was able to monitor the return of one species of malaria-carrying mosquito that had apparently been eradicated some years earlier.

The Umbugwe area, at the southern end of Lake Manyara, about twenty miles long and eight miles wide, bounded by the rift wall of the Mbulu mountains on the west and by the sparsely populated Masai country on the east, was inhabited by the Wambugwe, the smallest tribe in Tanganyika. Within Umbugwe, on the eastern shore of Lake Manyara, was the smaller traditional tribal area of Bugwe, which comprised of an area of salt-soda flats, almost free of vegetation, at the edge of the lake. It was like a desert in the hot season, the air shimmering with heat and mirages constantly appearing in the distance over the white earth. The people resembled Masai and, like them, were frequently seen carrying a shield and throwing spear. They were, however, of completely different ethnic origin, being Bantu and not Nilo-Hamitic like the Masai whose land surrounded much of theirs. The Wambugwe* were, however, easily recognized by a single long and deep tribal scar running down each cheek. Elders told me that in the past their tribe had been raided by Masai for countless years and that they had survived by avoiding surprise attacks and building their houses to withstand attacks when they did occur. They therefore built houses no higher than eye level in the completely open terrain provided by the salt-flats, thus giving them all-round visibility at all times. Their traditional houses, which were still in the majority, were called 'tembe'. They were built like little fortresses and were above five feet high, with flat roofs slightly sloping down to the back. They were nearly square in shape and quite large, for their average length well exceeded thirty feet. The manner of construction of tembe made them extremely difficult to be set alight by burning spears which had been widely used in the past in tribal attacks on villages. Their walls were constructed of stout wooden stakes, closely set together and daubed with a mixture of mud and cow dung. The understructure of the roof was composed of the stalks of red millet placed across wooden beams. The outer surface of the roof was made of thick pieces of turf placed upside down and covered with a layer of earth. Each tembe had a single small doorway that could only be entered by stooping low, thereby presenting a vulnerable target to any Mbugwe defender indoors. In most tembe, a spear and shield was customarily kept on the undersurface of the roof just inside the doorway, the roots for this custom extending back to historical times when a high level of readiness was maintained for defence of the doorway.

The floor of the tembe lay slightly below ground level and the internal plan of the rooms was also largely based on historical requirements. There were typically five rooms for accommodation of cattle, sheep, donkeys and goats, and also the millet harvest, as well as the human inhabitants. The most important room was the millet store and kitchen, which was situated at the back of the

---

* Wambugwe is the plural form; Mbugwe is the singular.

tembe and reached at the end of a deliberately constructed maze provided by the other rooms and passages. The millet was stored in an enormous, woven-grass 'Ali Baba' basket and consisted of the grain harvest required to carry the household over from one year to the next. The cattle and other domestic animals were all stalled indoors at night, historically to protect them from Masai raiders, hyaenas and lions. I was told that while there was no longer any danger from Masai, there were still sufficient numbers of hyaena and lion in the area to present a slight threat to domestic animals if left unprotected outdoors at night.

Most of the 7,500 Wambugwe clung strongly to their traditional ways, there still being some 2,000 tembe within the Umbugwe area, but the hand of progress was apparent, particularly among the younger generation. With the threat of tribal wars no longer present, many lived beyond the salt-flats of the tribal area and among grass land for grazing their cattle, and closer to land for cultivating their sorghum crop. Tembe, when built, were higher than in the past, and some Wambugwe even built huts of the non-traditional banda type. Many of the men adhered to their traditional role of carrying spear and shield in defence of the tribe, guarding their cattle, hunting wild game, and fishing. The women worked extremely hard, particularly those who lived in the tribal area, for they had a long way to walk each day to cultivate their sorghum fields, to draw fresh water, and to collect firewood. Some men turned to cultivation but they were despised by their elders for doing what was traditionally women's work. The women also picked leaves from wild plants for cooking as vegetables and prepared 'ugali' using sorghum flour.

I worked amongst the Wambugwe for two years, studying the malaria-carrying mosquitoes and assessing malaria transmission. It took several days before my mosquito collecting team and I were accepted by the people and allowed to enter their tembe to collect mosquitoes. This was quite understandable as there were several tribes in the Magugu area and these were represented in the team with my chief field assistant being a Masai. There was, however, one Mbugwe in the team and the work became easier after I had made him spokesman. My Masai assistant soon became accepted and respected by the Wambugwe for the high level of supervision that he gave to the work. There was an outbreak of malaria in the Umbugwe area at the end of 1961 and early 1962, following exceptionally heavy rains in November 1961, and I monitored its transmission. Since Magugu was a focus for sleeping sickness, more than usual dispensary care was given there to the taking of blood-slides and microscopy, thus making available good parasitological data. Anti-malaria drugs were readily available at the Magagu government dispensary and the outbreak was short-lived.

Irene and I had a restricted social life during our first two years in Arusha as I spent several days each week on safari, either at Magugu or Taveta, and although we had an 'ayah', Irene would not leave the children at night. There was a government rest house at Magugu and the East African Institute of Malaria rest house at Taveta. I used both of these initially, but they were sited a little way from the field laboratories and experimental huts, and both required prior reservation, the former through the District Commissioner's office in Mbulu, and the latter through the Director of the Malaria Institute in Amani. Because of the frequency of my visits, it became impracticable to keep on using the rest houses, so CIRU stores issued me with a good ridge tent and other camping equipment and I took these on safari, pitching tent near the field laboratories. With the passage of time, two groups of laboratories and experimental huts were developed at Magugu, and villagers built houses near them with close access to their wells, naming them, respectively, 'Ciru' – pronounced Seeroo – and 'Vibau Vitatu' after a nearby sign-post showing directions of three tracks. In Taveta area, the site of the field station was generally called 'Kibalwa', as it was located near an already existing village of that name which had been selected because of its high mosquito population. I went on safari alone, but well stocked with food, drinking water and a jerry can of water for washing. Irene usually supplied me with an egg and bacon pie and a cake, frequently a chocolate one, and I took a small primus for making tea. Meals were supplemented by bananas and mangoes bought locally.

There was a desperate need for a nursery school in Arusha but one could not be established unless the teacher was qualified and registered to teach in Tanganyika. When it became known that

Irene was a qualified teacher, she was requested by the headmaster of Arusha School, and many mothers, to establish a nursery school. As Linda was three years old and Diana only one, Irene agreed to set up a nursery school within our own home and garden. In December 1959, she was given registration number EE/237, and her school registered as number E/47, by the Tanganyika Ministry of Education and Labour. She commenced with about a dozen pupils and within two years had over twenty pupils, with the demand for places so great that there was a waiting list. A section of the garden was developed as a children's playground, having a large sand pit enclosed by stout logs of blue gum trees obtained from nearby Olmotonyi. The sand pit was surrounded by compacted earth to form a 'speed track'. The playground also contained a see-saw of heavy loliondo wood, a wendy house constructed from offcuts normally used as firewood, two large old tyres half sunk in the ground to form a primitive trampoline, and a swing, with an old tyre as seat, suspended from a large fig tree overhanging the edge of the playground. Before long, Irene had amassed a mountain of play equipment, including pedal cars, tricycles, skooters, skipping ropes and inummerable buckets and spades for use in the sand pit. The extensive lawn area of the garden outside the playground was also used for organized children's games and Irene's whistle was frequently to be heard within the neighbourhood.

Indoors, the school furnishings and equipment were also developed from humble beginnings. Tables and chairs for twenty or more infants were made to order from the white missionary school, which had a carpentry training school at Ntemi River some fifteen miles from Arusha. There was an abundance of play equipment such as building bricks, soft toys and dinky cars, but Irene's immense popularity among the mothers rested as much on her teaching ability as on her proficiency as a nursery school supervisor. Parents were also pleased to know that she was a qualified teacher and registered to teach in Tanzania. She acquired a reputation for getting children off to a good start, both in numbers and in writing, so much so that prior attendance at Irene's school was taken into account favourably by the headmaster of the prestigious government Arusha School when considering applicants. With Irene's high social standing and my frequent absences on safari, it was not surprising that during my first two years in Arusha. I was generally known as 'the husband of Mrs Irene Smith'.

Irene's hours were nine to twelve from Monday to Friday, although several mothers were inclined to deposit their children a little earlier and retrieve them a little later. Hence all was ready by 8.30 a.m., and prepared with military precision. The lounge was cleared with the help of cook, garden boy and ayah, tables and chairs were put in place, along with teaching and indoor play equipment and teaching materials, and the considerable quantity of sand pit and speed track equipment was arranged outdoors. Most children were collected by their parents soon after twelve when things were put away with equal precision, mostly into the third bedroom which conveniently had a door of its own leading onto the back veranda. Irene charged a ludicrously small fee, even by the standard of those days, of twelve shillings a week per child, with refunds for days absent. The fees hardly paid for the upkeep of the school, but they provided wonderful facilities and a playgroup for Linda and Diana as well as a source of friends, not only for our children but also for ourselves.

After two years of selecting and training staff in the field, I was able to spend less time away from Arusha and enter more into social activities. There was an Arusha rugby team which seemed to have difficulty in getting a full side together, so I had no difficulty in joining it despite having played only once during the previous twelve years. The one occasion occurred some years earlier when Irene and I had driven up from Gonja and were spending a weekend in Moshi. We saw a rugby field near the town with players warming up for a game so we joined the spectators, intending to stay for only a moment. A somewhat anguished player suddenly appeared and asked me if I could play rugby and make up the team as his side was a man short. I played right prop and enjoyed the game, although I was a bit stiff the next day. The Arusha team did not have regular practice games or fixtures, so I was unable to maintain the necessary level of fitness to easily withstand the knocks and tackles on frequently hard playing surfaces. Nevertheless, I played rugby for two seasons and Irene accepted the team's rugby jerseys for washing and repair after each match. I played almost every position on the field, the last one being full back in North versus South

1. Traditional onion-shaped huts (Tuku) on Ukara Island, southern Lake Victoria, 1951

2. The author collecting mosquitoes resting outdoors
in South Pare lowlands, Tanganyika, 1959.
(Photograph by Duncan Whitfield, FMPA)

3. Searching for mosquitoes resting under the eaves of a hut in South Pare, Tanganyika, 1959. (Photograph by Duncan Whitfield, FMPA)

4. The author writing up results at the field laboratory in South Pare, Tanganyika, 1959. (Photograph by Duncan Whitfield, FMPA)

5. The Smith family in their garden at Gonja Maore, South Pare, Tanganyika, 1959. (Photograph by Duncan Whitfield, FMPA)

6. Irene Smith with
Dr Trant pounding maize,
South Pare, Tanganyika,
1955

7. Irene with Mpare mother
and children, 1955

8. Medicine horn and tip of another horn used for cupping, South Pare, Tanganyika, 1956

9. Examining mosquitoes collected from houses in a village in Ogum State, Nigeria, 1963

played at Dodoma. The decision to stop playing rugby finally rested on the high cost of maintaining my car. Most of the players did not have cars, and driving six rugby players over pot holes between Arusha and Dodoma or Mombasa became more than I could afford, although some of the players worked at Riddoch Motors in Arusha and tried to keep my costs down.

The local gun club must also have had difficulty in getting a full team together for I was soon approached to join it. I did so for about a year under the enthusiastic leadership of Sir Lionel Fletcher, a charming old boy who farmed at Himo. On Sunday mornings we would collect the team's .303 rifles from the police station armoury and shoot at the butts which were situated very near Arusha. I held my place in the team and even won a small silver medal which Linda wore as a pendant for several months. However, the need to get up early every Sunday morning to be at the butts at 8.30 a.m. eventually became a bit much, since Sunday was the only day in the week that I did not have to be at work by 7.30 a.m. I therefore considered resigning from the club to enjoy the bliss of an extra hour in bed, but was pre-empted by its being disbanded some months prior to Tanganyika becoming independent in 1961.

Sir Lionel Fletcher died a few years later and Irene and I were invited to his former house where some of the contents were being offered for sale. The house was a sizeable, but unpretentious, farmhouse situated in the bleak and usually dusty surroundings of a large sisal plantation near the village of Himo. Lady Fletcher greeted us on arrival and invited us to tea. She was elderly, slim, carried herself with considerable poise, and spoke with a slightly foreign accent which I could not place. With a somewhat detached manner, she took us into two rooms and indicated that all pieces were for sale at thirty shillings each. The first room contained a number of large blue and white bowls and oddly shaped vases standing on a table, and the extensive pelmets were ringed with mainly large blue and white plates and dishes, but also several large, coarsely coloured plates. These had no appeal so we passed into the second room after I had looked at the back of one dish which bore several incomprehensible squiggles in blue.

In the second room, there was a glass cabinet and tables bearing a great variety of small items. There were a lot of minute carvings of birds and animals in what appeared to be green stone, and somewhat larger carved animals in jade; a number of netsuke and small ornamental photograph frames and clocks; some rather peculiar spoon-like objects in blue and gold; several old faded icons on wood or with additional ornamentation in silver and gold. There were some beautiful small boxes with gold and enamel patterning, and two larger boxes that appeared to be made of papier mache, the tops of which had scenes painted on them. I asked Lady Fletcher about these boxes and she replied warmly that the tops depicted scenes of old Russia and were painted by well known artists. One was a sleigh scene, and Lady Fletcher enthused over the beauty of Russia in the winter. The glass cabinet contained some figurines, including one like a harlequin, and two small teapots, one illustrated with oriental scenes and with a domed lid attached to the spout by a rather ugly chain. Its base was marked with 'AR' in very bold, blue lettering. The other teapot was round with a flat lid, but had a nice little finial the shape of an apple, and I bought it for Irene. There were six cups and saucers which looked much alike, although Lady Fletcher remarked that she liked the three with swan-necked handles. The bases all had different markings in blue including 'AR', 'KPM', and 'KHC', and crossed swords which differed in small matters of detail, except for one cup which had a mark like a caterpillar. The cups looked a bit fragile for service in Africa, so I turned my attention to six plates in the cabinet. Three had blue rims ornamented with butterflies, sprays of flowers in the centre, and were marked 'Royal Crown Derby'. The other three plates were brightly patterned in gold, red and green, with the centre blazoned with the family crest of Fletcher – a dexter arm in armour embowed and holding an arrow in fess. As a memento, it seemed appropriate to have the crested plates, so I bought them and also the very British-looking Royal Crown Derby ones. The cabinet also contained two ornamental eggs, one of pale blue glass about the size of a duck's egg, with a bright ribbon attached to it and bearing the initials 'AS'. As these were my own initials, I expressed interest in buying it but Lady Fletcher declined, saying that these were the initials of a royal personage. She offered me the other egg which was of lightly engraved silver, about the size of a pigeon's egg, and contained in an oval, red, velvet box fitted with a small, gilded clasp. Unlike the teapot and plates, the egg had no aesthetic appeal but I bought it out of curiosity. I would have liked several other items but, because of recent heavy repairs to my car, my cash-flow situation did not allow it.

When next on home leave, I took the egg to Wartski in Regent Street where it was explained to me that, although the egg was a Faberge one, it was not a valuable imperial one, the *workmeister* 'OM' who made the egg being one of five hundred in the house of Faberge which turned out vast numbers of inexpensive pieces as well as fewer costly ones. I accepted his offer of thirty pounds for it and Irene and I had a day out in London on the proceeds. We still enjoy having the teapot and plates although they too are of no great value. The teapot was professionally identified as an early nineteenth century Vienna one, the Royal Crown Derby plates were dated 1902, and the crested plates as early nineteenth century Ridgeways. Nevertheless, those two rooms in Himo probably contained many of what would now be extremely valuable pieces of Meissen, Ming and Faberge available for only thirty shillings each.

Irene and I joined the Arusha Gymkhana Club which constituted a major social centre, not only for Arusha residents but also for members living several miles out of town. There were some three hundred members, predominantly British because most Asians, Greeks and Italians preferred being members of their own clubs, and, before independence, very few Africans could afford or indeed wanted to be members of clubs. The Arusha Gymkhana Club had a thriving tennis section, with Kay Hocking as Tennis Member of the Club Committee. Irene had played club tennis but the game was virtually new to me. However, Kay persuaded me to attend the mix-ins which were held each Wednesday late afternoon, and little by little I picked up the game. In the years that followed, Irene and I played a lot of tennis and won several trophies. After independence, many Asians joined the club to play tennis. Among them were some extremely good players who helped to raise my game and included me in many of their foursomes so that for several years I was playing four days each week. In 1965 Abdhul Maharali and I won the men's open doubles. Abdhul was an outstanding player and a perfect gentleman on the court. I also played many singles and for years had most enjoyable, and often very long, sets with Max Hofer and Amir Somji. I also had many memorable singles with Max Corbett and Ron Taylor, successive ministers at Christ Church, Arusha, and John Owen, OBE, Director of Tanganyika National Parks.

Irene and I made many friends at the club through tennis and, shortly before Kay retired in 1966, I took over as Tennis Member. In addition to the usual annual competitions, Irene and I arranged, every month or two, a social event in the form of a one-day tennis tournament. Mixed pairs were matched as evenly as we could and all pairs played one another. The tournament usually started quite early and finished late, broken only by a lavish tea supplied by the lady players. Not infrequently, each pair played more than a hundred games in the glare and heat of the courts. Consequently, the tournaments were often quite exhausting, but they were extremely popular, with many of the participants obtaining great enjoyment in the days that followed from discussing their performance and their trials and tribulations during the tournament. It quickly became obvious that these tournaments provided a situation where players of different nationalities, men and women, felt at ease. Several Africans subsequently joined the club and played a good game of tennis, particularly 'Big' Bigirwenkya, Secretary General of the East African Community, and Noah Okulo of the same organization. We extended our club social activities to include an annual tennis 'ball', decoration strands being made up from extremely old and worn balls, tie-died Oxford or Cambridge blue.

The Colonial Insecticides Research Unit (CIRU), or Tropical Pesticides Research Institute (T.P.R.I.) as it was titled after independence, had a good workship which made the squeegees used by the tennis section for sweeping standing water off the courts. This practice was very much in keeping with the spirit of the times whereby business concerns, local farmers and government departments all helped out in maintaining the social life of the Arusha community. The squeegees had handles the length of brooms, but with heads like giant windscreen washers made from heavy duty pulley belt clamped between shaped boards. The ball boys, or 'tennis caddies', as they were later called, loved to fence with the squeegees, and a lot of thought went into designing squeegees that could stand up to this treatment. After independence, it became increasingly difficult to obtain imported goods, and balls and nets had to be purchased in Kenya. Fortunately, Tom Hedges, a keen tennis player and club secretary, frequently visited Nairobi and was able to buy these items from time to time, and Irene and I were able to extend the life of some of the old balls by scrubbing and drying them in the sun. There was also much sewing up of tennis nets in an effort to keep them intact; nevertheless, cries of 'through' were not infrequently heard. The three tarmac courts were always playable but varied considerably in condition, and players frequently moved from one court to another when the opportunity arose. I was therefore very pleased to oversee the re-laying of three courts during my term as Tennis Member. It was difficult to keep players off before the surface was sufficiently dry, and the courts had to be regularly dusted with fine grit for several weeks, even after playing was resumed. But what a difference it made; no bad patches, and for the first month or two the courts exhibited a much appreciated springiness in the heat of the day.

The Arusha Amateur Arts Society was essentially a very active amateur dramatic society with much of its talent being drawn from staff of Arusha School and the Tropical Pesticides' Research Institute. The society had its own 'little theatre', which had a small, sloping stage and plush red seating for an audience of about one hundred and fifty. There was also a small foyer which housed a popular bar, open during performances and sometimes during rehearsals. There were two dressing rooms and a toilet in a small back yard enclosed by a high wall. The building and premises had previously been a garage workshop but no signs of its former use was evident by the time I arrived in Arusha. Six plays were put on each year, allowing approximately six weeks for rehearsals, three days for performances, and a week or a little longer for auditions for each play. The seats were comfortable and the acoustics good, except during heavy rain when stage voices were slightly muffled by the sound of drumming on the corrugated iron roof. Theatre parties preceded by dinner were popular, and before independence evening dress was quite often worn, particularly on the last night.

I had not taken part in amateur theatricals since my schooldays, when I played Crampton in a public performance of Bernard Shaw's 'You Never Can Tell' in the town hall of Ashby-de-la-Zouch. My main recollection of it was that it involved a lot of time and work, and I vowed from then on not to get involved in acting again. With the passage of years, I had forgotten this schoolboy vow by the time I reached Arusha, and when there was some difficulty in filling a minor role among a large cast in a Christmas pantomime, I took the part of a cook who briefly appeared on stage in a slapstick act with colleague Norman Crossland and teacher Ken Wigmore. I had no dialogue but merely threw dough about the stage and joined my two companions in a seasonal rendering of 'Mud, mud, glorious mud'. Senior colleague George Burnett was the producer. In addition to producing many plays, George showed great facility at stage carpentry, which, allied with Joan's very considerable talent as a painter, led to sets that greatly enhanced productions and contributed to the success of our little theatre over more than a decade. The following year, George produced an 'Old Tyme Music Hall' with a large cast and I played the extremely brief and silent part of the strong man, Professor A.L.E.C. SMITH who, dressed in a leotard, lifted heavy weights with much grunting and groaning and, after receiving due admiration from the audience, left the stage with two small scene shifters carrying the weights behind him. My next appearance on stage was again silent and brief, the part being a diner in the background of 'Separate Tables' in which Joan and 'Dusty' Miller gave magnificent performances in the lead parts.

The Little Theatre had an active committee, with Colonel Bert Weston, OBE, as President. He was widely known as the 'Purple Emperor' because of his ruddy complexion and large physique. Shortly after the 'Old Tyme Music Hall', the committee lost its house member and Bert Weston persuaded me to fill the vacancy since the post was not very demanding in time or effort. It required me to keep the premises clean with the help of a theatre boy, or 'steward', as he was called after independence. My other duties included rolling down the red carpets between aisles the day before a production was to go on, ensuring that the toilets worked and that the seats were all serviceable, keeping the fire extinguishers in working order, and getting pictures of each production framed and hung in the auditorium. The theatre steward, Mohamed, and I worked well together and I stayed as house member until leaving Tanzania on retirement. In the course of cleaning out cupboards, we came across a pile of photographs of previous productions stretching back for years. Irene and I carefully mounted them and they were framed and hung in the foyer and auditorium providing great interest to the audience between acts. Another duty was to carry the bouquets of flowers on stage and present them to the actresses before the final curtain.

The plays were almost invariably a great success, drawing room farces being particularly popular under the production of George Burnett, Kay Hocking, Kathleen and Ernest von Roretz, and, later on, Clive Rushbrook, all of whom often combined producing with acting. Most plays only just broke even as the box-office takings barely covered the cost of the fine sets and costumes, but each year usually ended well in credit due to the Christmas pantomime or play which was performed for five days and well attended throughout. The great thing about farces was that rehearsals for them were often hilarious and I was frequently reduced to bouts of painful laughter. Most players took a very light-hearted attitude to their acting, but there were a few who took their roles very seriously and were greatly affected by any review of their performance published in the local newspaper.

My next appearance on the stage was in the Christmas play of 1964, which was 'Toad of Toad Hall', produced by Philip Evans, with the extremely talented young teacher, Clive Rushbrook, as Musical Director. Somewhat unexpectedly, I was cast in the role of Mole – not, I suspect, because of any indication of acting ability, but because of the costume that Irene made for my final audition. She made a magnificent Mole's head-piece of black cloth stretched over a wire frame and fitted with pince-nez spectacles, also made from wire. The whole head-piece fitted over my head, allowing me to see dimly through the loose mesh of the cloth. This poor visibility frequently required me to peer around to locate my opposite number on stage and was misconstrued by the audience as acting. Children in the audience, and there were many home for the hols, loved the head-piece as they could easily distinguish me as Mole. Between rehearsals, my daughters Linda and Diana, then eight and six years old, would each place the head-piece on in turn and, supporting the snout with their hands, run round the house squeaking with delight. The play was a great success, much of it due to colleague Colin McKone who was a very good actor and gave a magnificent performance as Toad. Irene also made her debut as Chief Ferret and was much acknowledged by the audience.

The following Christmas performance was the pantomime 'Little Red Riding Hood' produced by Kay Hocking, with Clive Rushbrook as musical director. My younger daughter, Diana, made her debut in a woodland scene, alternating between the roles of Sprite and Pigeon. I played the villainous agent, Colonel Fogey, with Hosea Isige as a corrupt businessman and my partner in numerous dastardly deeds. Hosea entered into the spirit of the play, showing many expatriates for the first time that an African could give a first-class performance on stage if he so wished. There were several beneficial 'spin-offs' from his participation in the play. As a newcomer to Arusha, he got to know socially quite a number of expatriates, including colleagues from work, and he extended his English vocabulary to include idiomatic expressions. Working relationships with him at the Tropical Pesticides' Research Institute were also facilitated by having laughed and joked together on stage.

By the end of 1966, many of the players who formed the mainstay of the Little Theatre had left Tanzania and there had been an influx of young ex-pats, mostly British, quite a number of whom held different views from those of their predecessors on social matters, including appropriate plays to be staged in the Little Theatre. Indeed, a few perceived the Little Theatre as an enclave of old colonials performing peculiarly British drawing room farces, having no relevance to the social life of Tanzania and being entirely inappropriate for the times. Audiences were also becoming more international. In response to changing times, the next year or so was devoted to other types of plays. I took part in two of them, largely because of the difficulty in filling parts as not enough new players were coming forward to replace the loss of the old ones. I took the part of the judge in 'The Ant Hill', which was a clever farce written by a distinguished Nigerian playwright. The play was too subtle for most of the audience, though, receiving polite silence throughout most of the performance and diplomatic applause on completion. The other play was 'Our Town', by Thornton Wilder, in which I played Mr Webb, my mid-west accent apparently being acceptable as I had based it on that of Tom Macmillan, a Baptist missionary with whom I often played tennis. Nevertheless, the audience was small and the play was received with the customary diplomatic level of applause. It did, however, have the redeeming feature that the producer, Connie Sieck, was extremely attractive and her presence probably doubled the size of the audience on the last night.

Towards the end of 1968, the inadequate income obtained from the small audiences over the previous year had so impoverished the theatrical society that it decided to go back to staging some of the more popular plays in amateur theatricals, including drawing room farces. Concurrently, nearly all the older players had left Arusha by this time and several young ex-pats, who had changed their perception of the Little Theatre, developed a great enthusiasm for amateur theatricals. In the following years, before I left Arusha in November 1972, they put on some of the best and most amusing productions that I have ever seen. I played Commander Rimmington in 'Chase Me Comrade' and took the part of the villain, Colonel Kali, in 'Red Riding Hood', the Christmas pantomime of 1969 (Irene played Grannie and sang 'Those were the days my friend'). The fortunes and popularity of the Little Theatre were not merely restored, but even increased, as the reputation of the society grew for putting on amusing and entertaining productions. More children came to see the plays, including African children whose parents were employed in the growing inter-governmental East African Common Services Organization which had established its headquarters in Arusha. Their parents also sometimes came along and many clearly enjoyed the so-called 'English' comedies, acquiring a few useful idiomatic expressions along the way. One colleague, for example, was wont to utter 'Stone the crows!', an expression derived from a pantomime, and used with great effect. The following year, I played Malvolio in Shakespeare's *Twelfth Night* and Irene made all my costumes. It was a major and costly production but played to packed audiences, including many Africans and Asians to whom the name of Shakespeare was well known and who were curious to see one of his plays.

Irene, my elder daughter Linda and I took part in the 1971

Christmas play which was 'A Christmas Carol', produced by Roger Wesson. Irene was the storyteller and Linda, who was home for the hols, took the part of Dora at a moment's notice. Philip Daniels and Emma Shitacha gave outstanding performances as Bob Cratchit and Tiny Tim respectively, and I enjoyed playing the part of Ebeneezer Scrooge. By 1972 there had been significant Africanization of posts previously held by ex-pats, and while quite a number of Africans regularly watched performances, most had no interest in taking part in amateur theatricals. Many were living in exciting times with their careers and futures in the melting pot. Their social life was therefore by necessity largely devoted to strengthening important social ties among themselves, leaving them no time for rehearsals. Consequently, although audiences were quite large, it became difficult to obtain sufficient actors, producers and backstage help to mount enough plays for the theatre to be run economically. It had been possible to put on only three plays by October, when Irene and I gave our last performance before leaving Arusha in November. Irene played Private Susie Tidmarsh and I had the part of Corporal Sydney Green in the comedy, 'The Amorous Prawn', produced by Di Bannister and Les Hammond. Although the Arusha Amateur Arts Society was again going through a rough patch, comedies and farces were still the most popular plays, and British ex-pats continued to be the main source of actors and producers.

Occasionally, while I was doing odd jobs as house member in the Little Theatre, government officials would enter the foyer or auditorium and I would welcome them, tell them that membership was open to all, explain what took place in the theatre, sometimes showing them around and inviting them to come to the next production. It was apparent that the Tanzanian government took a benign view of the society and had shrewdly assessed that it provided a harmless outlet for expatriates after working hours.

When Linda was five years old, she went to the Arusha School which provided education up to the age of thirteen years, after which children generally went on to a secondary boarding school education in Tanganyika, Kenya or the United Kingdom. Cyril Hampshire was headmaster, as he had been for several years. The school had a reputation of high standing, not only as a teaching establishment but also for its good public school atmosphere, discipline, and association with the Christian church. Its buildings were impressive in spacious grounds, and its teachers and pupils nearly all British expatriates. Africans, Indians and Greeks had their own schools where teaching included their own national languages. Irene continued with her nursery school until Diana was five and accepted into Arusha School. Cyril Hampshire had retired and had been succeeded by the Reverend Bryn Jones, who was a fine headmaster as well as a minister and had the difficult task of smoothly africanizing the school with regard to both its teachers and pupils. The official government view regarding most institutions was that africanization would proceed on the basis that there would be no lowering of standards, only a change. By 1965, most of the expatriate teachers, on pensionable terms of employment, had taken golden handshakes and early retirement under the Tanzanian government's africanization programme, the intention being that vacant posts would be filled by Africans. However, in spite of great efforts to obtain qualified African teachers through the Tanganyika Education Department and East African Public Services Commission, Bryn was not successful and had to recruit staff locally, if possible, or expatriate staff on short-term contracts. With both children in full-time education at Arusha School, Irene was available to join the school staff and, by arrangement with Bryn, taught the first form while Diana was entered at second form level so that there could be no conflict between teaching and mother/daughter relationship.

Open school events, such as sports day and Christmas carols, were maintained and were as popular as ever, although small modifications were sometimes required to adjust to staff shortages. For example, I usually swam for the parents' side but occasionally had to make up the staff team. One of Irene's duties was to teach swimming but, as she could not swim, arrangements were made for her timetable to coincide with one of my free evenings when I stood in for her. Linda and Diana learnt to swim in Arusha and both became fine swimmers in a very short time. The young British expatriate teachers who joined were almost without exception a great asset to the school and to the community, and helped to maintain the efficient and happy atmosphere in the classroom for which the school had long been renowned.

The whole subject of education became a big issue in Tanzania shortly after independence, enhanced by President Nyerere himself having once been a school teacher. Even as President, he was frequently addressed as 'mwalimu' (i.e. teacher) and regarded as such by all Tanzanians, old and young. There was much public debate on what form education should take in the country now it was free from the 'yoke' of colonialism and was committed to a nation-building programme in which great emphasis was placed on self-reliance. Concern arose among expatriates that in the near future school curricula, when adjusted more to national requirements, would not provide for entrance into good senior schools outside Tanzania. St. George's Boarding School in Iringa, Tanzania, no longer seemed an option, although for girls the Kenyan schools, Loretta Convent and Kenya High, still maintained a good reputation and some expatriate girls still went on from Arusha School to one of these. Most British expatriates, who were entitled to educational allowances and passages for their children, sent them to boarding schools in the U.K., where continuity of education for them was perceived as more certain than in East Africa. Irene and I shared this view and, in 1966, when Linda was ten and Diana was eight, we sent them to Ashford School in Kent after reviewing a detailed list of many possible schools. Ashford School was selected because it was spoken well of by the wife of an old colleague who had sent her daughter there, it had an excellent record for obtaining academic success, it had both senior and preparatory classes enabling Linda and Diana to enter the same school together, it supervised overseas' pupils travelling between school and airport, and it looked after the school trunk during hols. The latter was an important consideration as many schools insisted that the school trunk should be collected at the beginning of each holiday, thereby causing much anguish to parents living far away. Also, the fees, although high, were not excessive. A further benefit was that Ashford was not far from Burgess Hill where their Uncle Ron and Aunt Nancy lived who would look after them during half-term hols.

While most schools in Tanzania rapidly adopted a markedly national curriculum, that of Arusha School, while no means untouched, was allowed to remain more traditional, in order to provide an acceptable education for the children of expatriate Kenyans and Ugandans stationed in the Arusha headquarters of the East African Community established there in 1967. The large Asian community, who spared nothing to ensure the best possible education for their children, were quick to appreciate the advantages of Arusha School and, in the prevailing climate of Afro-Asian solidarity, entered their children into the school in such numbers that within a few years asianization rather than africanization of the school had been achieved.

Concurrently, there were a number of staff changes. Irene converted to part-time teaching so that she could give more time to supporting social activities associated with my work, and Bryn Jones retired, the position of headmaster remaining vacant for several months, and being brilliantly filled in the interim by Clive Rushbrook as acting headmaster. Much to most people's surprise, the post was not filled by an African but by an Australian. He brought a breath of fresh air to the running of the school and clearly had no time for 'outmoded colonial attitudes', an expression which at that time ensured almost ubiquitous instant approval. He was a person of high principle and well-liked, but his apparently inadequate understanding of African attitudes led to a confrontation with senior Tanzanian officials and his leaving his post unexpectedly and at short notice. He was by no means the first disenchanted idealist that I had seen leave in this fashion. Fortunately, the school still had the highly experienced Ken Wigmore, who effectively acted as headmaster for a long time until the post was substantively filled.

In addition to tennis and amateur theatricals, there was a very active social life centred around the church, The Women's Service League, the club, and private lunch and dinner parties. Christ Church was a small, classically Anglican, stone building, open to all denominations and blessed with fine ministers who came from either Australia or New Zealand. Irene was the Sunday School superintendent for several years. Sunday School was always well attended, for it was held at the same time as morning service, and parents were pleased to have a time of uninterrupted devotion while their children were having their own period of religious instruction. Every year, the children presented a nativity play in the Church. As producer, Irene was able to draw on children of many nationalities, thereby giving the performance a truly international character. During a dress rehearsal for the 1971 nativity play, a visitor entered the church and asked if he could photograph the performance. Some months later, he sent Irene a copy of the Finnish magazine 'Totto', with the front cover displaying the children gathered around the crib. Irene still treasures the copy as it reminds her of many children and parents whom she knew in Arusha. One December there was a crisis with the nativity play when the father of all three kings was deported at a moment's notice. The situation was saved within a few days of the performance when three children, returning from the U.K. for their Christmas holidays, volunteered to help Irene out.

Irene was also a member of the parish council and of the Women's Guild committee. The Women's Guild held regular monthly meetings and raised money in support of several charities and organizations, one of which was the Buigiri Blind School. Irene and her friend, Molly Long, organized a dance at the New Arusha Hotel to raise funds for the blind school. Weeks and weeks of planning were involved, including persuading local traders and businesses to contribute raffle prizes, hiring a local band, and finding a personable M.C. At the beginning of the evening, the M.C. thought he would get the event moving by announcing a novelty elimination dance called 'Crossing the River'. Lines were drawn across the floor to represent the banks of a river and when a couple approached a line the man was required to pick up his partner and carry her across. When the music stopped any couple caught in the 'river' was 'out'. Irene was asked to dance by a new staff member of the Tropical Pesticides' Research Institute. As he approached the river, he enthusiastically swept Irene up in his arms, slipped, lost his balance, dropped Irene on the floor and fell heavily on top of her. Irene was knocked unconscious and laid on a settee in an adjacent room. Her partner held his head, lamenting, 'Why does it always happen to me?'. Molly Long arrived at the dance to see the unfortunate young man sitting at a table with his head in his hands. She laughingly said, 'Don't worry Howard, it may never happen'. He lifted his head and in some distress replied, 'But it has

– I have dropped Irene on her head and she is unconscious'. Molly was very distressed and immediately burst into tears. Irene recovered consciousness and I took her home where she was examined by a doctor and found to be lightly concussed, but after a couple of days in bed she fully recovered. Howard brought flowers round in the morning after the dance which, after its inauspicious beginning, was a great success and raised considerable funds for the blind school.

During the years following Tanganyika's independence, President Julius Nyerere made a great effort to promote self-reliance among Tanganyikans. In conformity with this policy, importation of many goods, including toys, was prohibited or severely restricted. Arusha Churchwomen's Guild organized sewing mornings to design and make toys. Members of the guild contacted people in the Arusha community who willingly donated balls of wool, lengths of ribbon, pieces of material, beads, and anything else which would be useful for making toys. Some members drew patterns, painted, knitted or sewed. Others cut up old material such as stockings or tights and made stuffing for the toys. Some fathers even found a hidden talent for making toys from odd pieces of wood. By Christmas each year, the guild was able to hold a magnificent toy fair, open to all. There were beautiful toys of all sizes, most reflecting the widely known animal life in East Africa, including giraffes, lions, elephants and rhinoceros, but other animals such as bears and pandas were also included, as well as fairy-tale characters like Humpty Dumpty. Rag dolls of various sorts were also extremely popular. The money obtained from each toy fair was divided between church funds and charities supported by the church. Of more direct importance than the financial side of the project was the close bond forged between women of different nationalities who met at the regular toy-making sessions, and the availability of toys at Christmas to many children who would otherwise have had none.

Another organization that made an excellent contribution to the social life of women in Arusha was the Women's Service League, which also supported charities and social activities, including running a public library and holding an annual flower show. With its superb climate and fertile volcanic soil, Arusha was a gardener's paradise. The annual flower show was therefore a colourful and prestigious event, keenly contested in all its classes of exhibits. A very popular class was that for children's exhibits. When quite young, Linda and Diana enthusiastically submitted exhibits, once constructing animals from vegetables, and, on another occasion, making attractive miniature gardens. The most coveted prize was the 'Gold Cup', originally presented to the League by S. Gold and frequently won by Dr Saska's wife, who grew magnificent flowers on a large scale for marketing. In the year that the league was disbanded following independence, Irene won the Gold Cup with five splendid 'Diamond Jubilee' roses from our garden. Not only did she receive the usual miniature replica awarded on these occasions, but she was also given the actual Cup for permanent retention.

After independence, it became increasingly difficult for Arusha hospital to maintain its blood bank because of heavy demands on it. This arose from more frequent road accidents as the amount of traffic and the number of inexperienced drivers increased. Another factor was that the number of voluntary blood donors decreased as the expatriate population diminished, since the old fear of 'mumiani' still lingered in some African minds. The situation became so desperate that an updated register was needed of volunteers prepared to have their own blood typed and to give blood regularly to the blood bank or act as donors in an emergency. In consultation with the hospital and with my support, Irene took on this difficult and unpopular task, the eventual updated register not unexpectedly comprising most T.P.R.I. and Arusha School staff members. Nevertheless, a very good relationship was always maintained between hospital professional staff and voluntary workers, even though, as the years passed, British doctors and nursing staff were almost completely phased out.

Arusha Gymkhana Club had over one hundred and sixty members, most of whom were British expatriates until independence in 1961, after which many more Asians joined, primarily to play tennis. Africans were very slow to join the club for several reasons: only a very few could afford the entrance fee and annual subscriptions; their social activities were largely centred around their own football clubs and bars where, in the politically exciting

112

times in which they lived, they could freely discuss day to day events; those who could afford to join the club were generally in senior positions and considered times much better spent, after hours, in building up potentially useful social and working relationships with new colleagues; finally, there was also a view that, as a largely British enclave, the club was not the right place to be seen, and that, in the course of nation building, it would have a very short future.

In May 1966, I was elected President of the club following a year as Vice-President, much of which was also spent as Acting President because of the unexpected overnight departure from the country of 'Bunny' Watts, the club President. With the help of Tom Hedges as Vice-President, a splendid committee and many supportive members, the club flourished. The golf section was very active, with the Golf Member, Derek Dehaaff, giving free lessons one evening each week and holding keen competitions for the monthly mug. The greatest expense to the club was maintaining the golf course, for East African weeds such as soddomm apple constantly threatened the fairways and damaged the gang mower, requiring it to be frequently serviced. The fairways and greens, in particular, were also pitted by the hooves of cattle grazed by the Warusha, a local Nilo-hamitic tribe closely affiliated to the Masai. Fortunately, the club bar was well supported by the golfers and the profits from it largely offset the golf section's expenses. I continued as Tennis Member during the three years in which I was President. Tennis was at least as popular as golf, which did not have the same appeal to African and Asian members. The three courts were occupied most evenings with twice-weekly mix-ins regularly attended by about twenty players except in the rains when numbers fell off; and, as indicated in earlier pages, tournaments were extremely popular. The rugby section was brought to life by Trevor Peregrine who, as Rugby Member, maintained a full programme of matches, by which time I had stopped playing rugby but was very pleased to support it. The club had a good billiards room with two full-sized tables and an active billiards section, with Wally Bransby-Williams as Billiards Member. Each year there were several tournaments and matches, including one against an Arusha Indian team, and a competition for the club Dingo Redfearn Snooker Cup.

Apart from each member's entrance fee of one hundred shillings and subscription of thirty shillings per month, the main source of club revenue was the bar. The club had an African barman, 'Coleman', who lived on the club premises in housing built for him a few yards away from the club. He was employed on permanent pensionable terms and, while members came and went, Coleman was always there, responding to the instructions of the Club Manager, Mr. Kuentslinger, and current Bar Member. The popularity of the bar seemed to vary in cycles but it excelled under the supervision of Chris Bannister who, as Bar Member, introduced daily bar snacks of bacon and eggs at virtually cost prices and an efficient roster of bar hours with the help of club members to assist at the bar. The club had a small library with an excellent choice of books selected monthly by the Library Member, Pat Jones, and her sub-committee. Chris Bannister made a brave attempt to maintain a monthly newsletter, but found there was too little club news to justify one each month, and so it was replaced by a quarterly one. There was an enterprising entertainments sub-committee with David Bassett as Entertainments Member. He arranged evening entertainments in bridge, darts and table tennis, and organized cinema shows, barbecues, childrens' Christmas parties and New Years' Eve balls. Swings were provided outdoors for the children near the existing club roundabout.

Thus, five years after independence, the Arusha Gymkhana Club was as popular as ever and apparently unaffected by Tanzanian government politics. However, on 19th October, 1966, it received a letter dated 10th October 1966 and signed by the Minister of Lands, Settlement and Water Development, Dar-es-Salaam. It stated that 'Notice is hereby given that the following land, namely all the piece or parcel of land, known as Arusha Gymkhana Golf Course, L.O. No.11099, Arusha, is required by the President for public purposes only, and notice is hereby given that the Minister intends to enter into possession of the said land at the expiration of two weeks from the date of this Notice'. With only five days to go before possession was due to take place, I informed the club committee and placed a large notice in the clubhouse advising members of the position and requesting them not to use the golf course after 23rd October. The reaction of the members, and particularly the regular golfers among them, was most supportive; no one played golf or used the course in any other way after that date. This immediate compliance undoubtedly saved the club from government sequestration and gave the committee time to consider how best to respond further to the government notice. I wrote to the Minister of Lands acknowledging his letter and requesting permission for golfers to use the golf course until such time as it was required by his Ministry. There was no response until about February 1967, when I received the reply that the course was required for nation building purposes but in the meantime the parcel of land could be used for 'golf qua golf'. This expression was mulled over in committee and, after obtaining legal advice, we concluded that it meant that the club could continue using the golf course and that approval was given for golf to be played on the course, but that it was to be used for no other purpose than golf. Golf was restored, although it took several weeks to get the course back into reasonable playing condition. The club members expressed their satisfaction at the next A.G.M. by putting forward my name only for President of the club!

The reinstatement of the golf facility to the Arusha Gymkhana Club was probably linked to the impending transfer of the East African Community Headquarters from Nairobi to Arusha and the need to provide suitable recreational facilities for senior staff of other nationalities. Certainly, within a year of the establishment of the Headquarters in Arusha in 1967, the club was well accepted by local Tanganyikan officials. 'Big' Bigirwenkya, the Secretary General of the East African Community, and several other senior African members of his staff, who were accustomed to playing in similar clubs in Kampala and Nairobi, joined the club, as did several senior Tanganyikans resident in Arusha, including John Malecela, Minister for Natural Resources. Within a short time Africans, although still a minority, became active and much-liked members of the club.

Lunch and dinner parties formed an important part of expatriate life, with a curry lunch at the weekend being almost an institution. This provided a pleasant social occasion for having guests of different nationalities; the lunch would often be served as a buffet and guests could take their meal and drinks outdoors if they wished. Curry lunches were often jolly and noisy, starting early, ending late, and much facilitated by generous libations of cold lager. Dinner parties were generally quite small, with two or four guests, and typically included a member from one's own department and his wife, plus visitors or someone outside from another department. They were also usually held to welcome new arrivals and entertain friends going on home leave.

Our Arusha house and garden provided an ideal setting for entertaining. Josiah the cook, Alice the house girl, and Jeremiah the garden boy, were all Wapare and worked together well to make our lunch and dinner parties a success. Once Irene had selected the menu, Josiah took over, with Alice serving at table and Jeremiah washing up. When dinner was ready, Josiah would sound the gong and we would go through the double doors leading from the lounge to the dining room, with its silver tableware gleaming in candlelight. After dinner, we would all move to the lounge and Alice would bring through the coffee and tea. The following morning we would enter the dining room to see the table laid for breakfast and no signs of the evening's entertainment, even when we had parties with about thirty guests. We held large parties for T.P.R.I. staff to meet distinguished overseas visitors and senior staff of the East African Community. These occasions had a fascination for Linda and Diana who were allowed to leave their beds for a moment to squint briefly through the lounge door at the arriving guests. Our most lively parties were our annual Christmas ones, when we had up to fifty guests and Irene was restricted to a budget of one thousand shillings. We had a buffet meal, with friends contributing plates of food, and drinks and glasses were set out for guests to help themselves after the first drink. The entertainment programme was much the same each year. We began with 'advertisements', in which twenty slightly mutilated advertisements were stuck on the walls and guests were given pencil and paper, and a small prize was given to the person who identified the most products advertised. The next game was 'tune titles' or 'film titles', four competing teams being required to identify the titles through drawings made by one of their team. There was 'passing the parcel' and 'nursery rhymes', the latter also being based on four teams competing to see who could sing the most rhymes. According to the time available, other games would also be played, such as 'charades', 'pass the orange' or 'musical chairs', but we always ended with a long and enthusiastic session around the piano.

Large scale entertainment by a servant's master was perceived as an indicator of the master's importance and reflected on the standing of his servants. Therefore, far from being an imposition on the servants, all this entertaining was much appreciated by them, for not only did they receive extra pay for the long hours involved and much of the food left over from the party, but also their standing was raised among their own circle of acquaintances.

Arusha had two cinemas, the Metropole and the Elite, both of which exhibited European and Asian films. Apart from the more senior Africans, who enjoyed European films, most Africans preferred the Indian ones as they were colourful and included more singing and dancing. Both cinemas had balconies which were largely occupied by Asians during performances of Indian films, and by Europeans during English-speaking films. Irene and I usually went to the cinema each Friday and tended to sit in the same seats in the Metropole so much that, after a few years, we were so associated with these seats that they were generally left empty for us each Friday night. The Metropole had indifferent sound equipment and, for several years, before the curtain was raised used to play a record which we could never make sense of. It sounded like 'fishin', but we eventually learned that the song was called 'Suspicion'.

Our first home leave from Arusha was in 1961. The Institute's houses had to be vacated before leave so that, in theory, they could be available for other staff members as required. In practice the houses were vacated but almost invariably kept empty for occupancy by the same staff member on his return from leave. Preparations for home leave commenced several weeks ahead with accumulation of sufficient boxes and old newspapers to pack up personal effects for storage. The week before going on leave, our home looked somewhat like a warehouse. On the day before leaving, the O/C Stores visited the house and took a furniture inventory, and the bulk of furniture and personal effects were transported by T.P.R.I. truck to one of the Institute's go-downs. We dined at a friend's house that evening. On the day of departure, the electric meter was read, the electricity turned off, the Institute's truck took away the remaining furniture and effects, and we locked up the house, giving the keys to the O/C Stores. We gave Josiah, Alice and Jeremiah each a good retainer and told them that I would write to Josiah from England informing him when to apply for the house keys for them to clean the house in preparation for our return. We then departed to Nairobi in official transport – a landrover estate wagon – and caught a late night flight arriving at Heathrow early the following morning.

We were met at Heathrow by a gleaming new two-tone-grey Ford Zephyr Mark II bought, as in 1956, on a 'home leave delivery plan'. Optional extras fitted included seat belts, kiddi-locks and overdrive. It was early summer and we had a fine drive to Guildford, the presence of a tarmac road being appreciated as much as the scenery. We stayed in a private hotel there for two weeks and then went on to Thorpe Bay, near Southend, to give Linda and Diana a holiday by the sea and also to be near Rochford, where Irene's mother and father had recently retired. We had most comfortable lodgings, whose owners' great wish over many years to conceive a child came true during our stay with them. They were greatly pleased, and our presence in some unjustified and unaccountable way was associated with this happy event. After a very pleasant, but otherwise uneventful leave, we returned to East Africa on the *Warwick Castle* with the new car in the hold.

Our vessel stopped at Gibraltar where we visited the rock to see its labyrinth of tunnels and famous apes. Linda and Diana loved the apes and we spent so long with them that we saw little else of Gibraltar. We bought both of the children a large 'walkie-talkie' doll at Genoa as these were very popular at the time. At Port Said, we enjoyed seeing the wares brought onboard by the Egyptian boat salesmen and purchasing two pouffes and a camel stool after much amicable haggling over prices. I had expressed an interest in seeing the pyramids, so when the opportunity of a tour from the ship arose, Irene and the children stayed onboard while I went on the tour, disembarking at Port Said and rejoining the ship at Port Suez. I enjoyed the ride on a camel towards the Sphinx and the Cheops pyramid, and marvelled at the fabulous Tutenkhamen artefacts in the Cairo museum. A guide showed us round the Great Mosque at Cairo and, possibly because of my knowing a few words of Arabic, he selected me to pass the hat round for him. The guide took our party into a souk displaying the usual mountains of brassware, rugs and leather goods, but I wandered away to see other shops outside the guide's chosen area. In one shop, I spotted a clearly second-hand and slightly damaged brass coffee pot but differing from all others, that I had seen, in having two lines of engraved script along one side. This gave the piece an added interest as I thought the script might be a quotation in Arabic. The shopkeeper tried to persuade me to buy other seemingly better coffee pots for the same price, but I stuck to my choice. On seeing my purchase, the guide became quite agitated and told me that I had made a bad purchase and should have stayed with his group. Some years later, I recognized the script as Hebrew, but it remained untranslated until thirty years later when, in retirement, I was able to have it deciphered through a friend in Bexhill. The script reads, 'Dedicated to the Israeli hospital and in the name of Aaron Halevi, son of Rachel deceased, and to his wife Zoffy, daughter of Frieda Waldheim, 13th day of the 9th month of the year 5709' (1949).

The remaining part of the voyage progressed smoothly with the usual shipboard activities of deck quoits, 'buckets', table tennis and fancy dress parade: Linda went as 'Criss Cross Quiz', Diana as a 'flying saucer', and I as a 'Cow and Gate baby' in company with a fellow passenger dressed as a nanny. The children enjoyed the crossing-the-line ceremony with Neptune's court, and being lathered, 'shaved' and dunked in the swimming pool by Neptune's attendants, one of whom was myself. During the general merriment, the barber threw the bucket of lather into the pool. The bucket hit me on the head inflicting a small wound requiring a stitch. The lesion was of no consequence, but I was a bit miffed at being charged ten shillings for having the stitch in and a further ten shillings for having it out. We disembarked at Mombasa and drove up to Arusha through Voi. Our house had been cleaned for our return and even the garden looked as if we had never been away. Josiah, Alice and Jeremiah were at the house when we arrived, but we had to stay overnight in the New Arusha Hotel until the next day when we could get our furniture and effects out of the Institute's go-down. Within a week, except for a few additional furnishings purchased on leave, our home looked as if we had never been away.

In the early 1960s, insecticide resistance among mosquito vectors of malaria was appearing at an alarming rate, jeopardising malaria eradication or control schemes in many developing countries. As Principal Investigator for Stage IV of the WHO Programme for Development of New Insecticides (primarily for replacing those against which malaria vectors had become resistant), my contacts with WHO staff in Headquarters had grown, and, in 1963, I was asked, through Kay Hocking, to go to Nigeria for three months as a WHO consultant. When administrative arrangements had been completed, including to ensure that I did not receive my East African salary as well as my consultant's fee, I flew to Lagos via Arusha and Nairobi, to be greeted by the Project Leader, Dr Bar-Zeev. I was taken to the West African Council Medical Research Laboratories compound at Yaba, on the outskirts of Lagos, and accommodated in an apartment in that compound. The consultancy involved identification and habits of mosquitoes frequenting villages near and around Lagos lagoon and, in cooperation with WHO consultant toxicologist, Dr. Vandekar, participation in insecticide trials at village level. I also gave a number of lectures to health workers.

I had left Arusha at the beginning of June, during the cool season, when the weather was perfect. The Lagos area, in contrast, was extremely hot and humid, with early morning being the only comfortable time outdoors. Most mornings, my team of mosquito collectors and I started in the field before dawn, breakfasting *en route* on hot corn-on-the-cob bought from one of the many roadside vendors at hand to service the stream of Africans walking to work in Lagos. I could not speak the local language, Yoruba, but my team spoke pidgin english for which I was grateful, although on some occasions I found it quite incomprehensible. It was also strange to be referred to as 'My Lord'. I enjoyed walking to villages scattered about the orchard-like countryside formed by the presence of cola-nut trees, and learned to accept, with respect, the frequent time-honoured gesture of friendship in receiving small pieces of cola-nut offered to me. Also interesting were the journeys by canoe to visit fishing villages around the shore of Lagos lagoon. Many houses were on stilts and projected over the water's edge. Some of the local population carried out pagan practices, including the worship of 'ibeji' – small wooden images – kept in sacred shrines in areas normally taboo to outsiders. Since local customs can sometimes affect the success of malaria vector control, I expressed a general interest in how extensive these shrines were and whether they were actually sited within villages or outside them. After some discussion between members of my team and villagers, a prominent villager said that he would take me to see one of the shrines, explaining that, since it would be taboo for my feet to touch the ground, he would carry me on his back. This he accordingly did for about a mile, arriving at a small arched inset in a grassy bank, containing two small wooden figures, their bodies daubed with red earth and their hair blue with indigo dye. We returned to the village where he explained that most shrines were similarly situated outside the village, and it seemed that they would not present a practicable problem in the event of village trials in the area. In practice, this was never put to the test, since (for purely entomological reasons) the project was transferred a few years later to another part of Nigeria.

Weekdays were busy and professionally interesting, but the weekends could have been dull had it not been for Drs. Chris and Kay Draper, previous colleagues in the Pare-Taveta Malaria Scheme in Tanganyika, now working on Yellow Fever at Yaba. They were keen members of the Lagos Yacht Club and invited me to crew with them on several occasions, with their two young daughters, Philippa and Alison, to one of the outer islands. It was a blessed release to escape the heat of the coast and to have congenial company. One weekend, one of my team took me to the ancient town of Abeokuta – 'the place under the rock' – to see the old tribal palace and its numerous relics. Some evenings the Yaba apartment would be visited by hawkers selling wares, including pieces which they described as 'very old, very good'. Bartering with them helped to pass the time, and eventually I bought a large pouffe, and two small ones for Linda and Diana: also two ibeji, one Yoruba and the other Ibo; two bronzes, one a head and the other a figure; and a wooden face mask with a long grass beard. Lagos museum gave me the necessary export permits and when I returned to Arusha, at the end of August, the mask was hung on a wall and the other pieces were placed above a window pelmet to remind me of my visit to Nigeria.

Irene and the children were well and had been kept an eye on by kind neighbours, particularly Jill and Simon Hocombe, who had visited Irene almost every evening to see that all was well. I was glad to be back in Arusha and even more glad that I had not accepted an offer from WHO of employment as a Project Leader. Out of the consultancy fees I bought Irene a small blue second-hand Fiat saloon which she called 'Bluebird' and which the rest of the family called 'Bug Box'. The main thing that suffered from my absence was my tennis, which took over a month to get back in shape. Shortly after my return, it became apparent that the beard of the face mask was an attractive site for resting insects, so I traded it in at a local curio shop for a set of coffee spoons. For some weeks it was displayed incongruously in the window of the shop, for tribal face masks had never featured as curios in Arusha nor Nairobi until then, and, as far as I was aware, nowhere else in East Africa. Eventually, it was sold and replaced by a newly-carved face mask of similar appearance, but without the beard. A few months later, the shop window displayed several recently carved masks of various designs and within a year most curio shops in Arusha and Nairobi were well stocked with face masks, some of them quite huge and grotesque.

One advantage of being a medical entomologist working in East Africa was that the dry season, when numbers of the main malaria-carrying mosquito were too low for field studies with insecticides, corresponded with the summer months in the U.K., thereby allowing the entomologist to go on home leave in the summer. Conversely, it was inappropriate to take home leave at other times, so I postponed home leave until the summer of 1964, which coincided with the year of the Zanzibar revolution. There was considerable disquiet at this time among expatriates in Tanganyika, because many expatriates in Zanzibar were having to leave at a moment's notice and it was thought that this might extend to the mainland. I took part in several packing parties in which people suddenly left Arusha, packing and removing their household effects within twenty-four hours. While the circumstances were sad for the people concerned, the atmosphere of packing parties was light-hearted, the helpers being well fortified with 'cakes and ale'. There was a tremendous demand for wooden crates. I had three large ones made, and obtained others over a period of several weeks from local shopkeepers, but mainly from Riddoch Motors where my old rugby connections with the staff there stood me in good stead. Many of the boxes had no tops, so I made these up from pieces of other boxes or from offcuts sold to me as firewood. Before departing for leave in May, our household effects were packed up in twenty-three heterogenous boxes and placed in the T.P.R.I. go-down, ready for overseas shipment should the occasion arise.

We travelled on the now familiar *Warwick Castle* and were met at London docks by a Ford Escort car which we had hired for the duration of the leave. We had an enjoyable drive to Milton Abbas in Dorset where we had rented one of the lovely old picturesque cottages in the high street. We arrived on a sunny day in May, the cuckoo was calling, and there was a captivating view of the village from the garden which rose steeply from behind the cottage. The thatched roofs of the eighteenth century cottages, lining each side of the road, where only broken by the fine old church, almshouse and village school. Like a nostalgic Victorian oil painting, nothing discordant was present and the overall impression was one of idealised rural tranquillity and beauty. Indoors, the cottage was ice-cold due to its thick walls of cob and having no damp course. With frozen fingers, I lit a fire and soon had it blazing away and we all moved in for one of our longest home leaves. Linda and Diana went to the local school at the top of the high street. They loved it and the teachers appeared to enjoy having them. School lunches arrived daily in a van and cost one shilling each. For the first time since the children were born, Irene and I were able to go out together for a few hours without them, so we often drove to Dorchester or Blandford Forum for lunch. Sometimes we took the lovely walk around the lake close to the bottom of the high street, near Milton Abbey Public School. At the weekends, we took the children to Studland Bay near Bournemouth, where there was a nice area of sand for them to play on; or to the Banbury Rings where they could slide down the banks of the old hill-top fort. They also enjoyed visiting Lulworth Cove and the swannery at Abbotsbury. Sometimes we had a cream tea in Cerne Abbas; knowing we were from East Africa, the proprietor, an old colonial, would greet us with 'Jambo, habari gani?' ('Hello, how are you?').

In June, an International Congress of Entomology was held in the Albert Hall and, as I was reading a short paper there, we all went up for a week, staying in a hotel near Kensington Gardens. Irene took the children to the Royal Tournament, the London Zoo, and to a cinema to see the first Beatles' film, 'A Hard Day's Night'. Travel on the top of a double-decker bus was a novelty for the children, and Diana entertained the passengers after announcing that she had come 'all the way from Africa'. One day, knowing Irene was in London, her former teaching colleagues arranged a tea party at the school where Irene had taught before we were married. Irene left Linda and Diana in my care. We had hardly entered the children's playground in Kensington Gardens when a royal helicopter descended in the grounds nearby. The bright red aircraft was like a magnet to the children and some fifty of them, including Linda and Diana, rushed towards the fence separating the royal grounds from Kensington Gardens. I lost Diana and, after searching for her for well over an hour, Linda and I dejectedly returned to the hotel only to find her playing in her room. It really was quite remarkable the way she had not only found her way back to the hotel, but also survived crossing the busy main road unaided.

Within a few weeks of our arrival at Milton Abbas, 'For Sale' notices appeared like mushrooms in several gardens in the village. This was our first contact with D.I.Y. enthusiasts and individual property developers. Our neighbour, who owned a semi-detached cottage, was busy removing Victorian plasterwork from the interior walls. He enthused over finding some sconces and was currently occupied in exposing the original inglenook fireplace. He offered us his house for £2,700; the owner of the detached cottage immediately below the church was prepared to sell his for £5,000. I saw a picture of this cottage, some years later, on the cover of a magazine.

We returned to East Africa by the *Pretoria Castle* and travelled by train from Mombasa to Arusha. There was the usual children's fancy dress party on board, to which Linda and Diana went as North American Indians. The sea journey was otherwise uneventful except for a guided tour of Pompeii to see the ruins and artefacts of that old Roman city. Diana, having heard an interesting item of conversation early in the tour, kept piping up with 'When are we going to see the dead men, daddy?'. Eventually her curiosity was satisfied when we saw the petrified figures in the museum.

In addition to home leave, normally granted every two years in Tanganyika, at the rate of five days leave for each month of service, a colonial officer was also eligible for two weeks local leave which had to be taken annually. Normally we would not have been able to afford to take local leave more than once a year, but unexpected sources of funds enabled us to take short leaves two or three times a year over three years. These funds arose from a small inheritance by Irene and two life insurance policies that I cashed in. The first was from a South African company which, after Tanganyika's independence, was prohibited from operating in Tanganyika; and the second was from a recognized company based in Nairobi which had decided after independence that the sum assured would be paid in local currency. I made sure that my third successive life insurance policy would be paid in the U.K. but by this time I was thirty-five and had to pay much higher premiums than for the other two policies.

I always took Irene and the children to the coast. The day of departure was always exciting. There was never enough room in the boot of the car after the inflatable boat, beach ball, buckets and spades, Irene's folding chaise longue, and food and water for an emergency had been included. The shelf below the back window of the car was heaped with children's toys and books. We drove through Taveta and on to Voi, where we always stopped at the Voi Hotel for a break and for the children to see the aviary there. The two hundred and fifty mile journey was generally dusty in July or August, arising from traffic ahead or passing on the murram road, but at Easter, and sometimes also at Christmas, it was often extremely muddy and, even with chains fitted on the rear wheels, there were times when the road was almost impassibile.

We first stayed at the Tudor House Hotel on Mombasa Island, taking an ayah, Rafikiole, with us. The children enjoyed the beach and watching the fiddler crabs on it. We visited Mombasa township and the old fort, and drove a little way up the coast to Nyali beach where the coral sand was as white as flour and the sea warm, green, and alive with wonderfully coloured fish and sea urchins. In subsequent leaves there was no need of an ayah and, apart from one leave spent at Malindi, we stayed at hotels along Nyali beach, the first being 'Ocean View' which was ideal for very young children, having a safe sandy play area near the beach. The children also loved the hotel's tree house and taking turns to sound the chimes announcing meal times.

The following leave we stayed at 'Whitesands', a little further up the coast. Here we found our Shangri-La, revisiting it time after time. We had accommodation in a grass thatched banda set among palm trees at the edge of the shore and with the soft white sand extending right up to the doorway. In the cool of dawn, Irene and I would make love, and afterwards I would run down the beach to swim in the warm, green, bouyant sea. The main rooms of the hotel were very near and of simple construction, the dining room having no walls, a concrete floor, and a makuti roof, but set among palms and glorious white sand and offering a wonderful view of the beach and sea. Next to the dining room was a small enclosure with two large tortoises, and Linda and Diana loved riding on their backs. In the daytime, Irene would often get established with a good book in her chaise longue placed in the shade of a palm tree and fulfil the important function of looking after the children's things (i.e. buckets and spades, tyres, clothes, towels, sun tan oil and medicaments for treating sun burn).

Except during mealtimes and the hottest hours of the afternoon, when we kept out of the sun, the children and I were contantly on the beach or in the sea. We walked long distances along the beach and I subjected them to many practical and theoretical aspects of marine biology, the most important one being early recognition of the spiny sea urchin which was abundant in shallow pools and whose urticarious spines could inflict most painful wounds. There were several sorts of crab, (including hermit crabs), brilliantly coloured starfish, interesting sponges, sea cucumbers, sea squirts, beautifully coloured fish, sea slugs, sea anemones and an enormous variety in size and shape of sea shells. We had a bright blue and orange inflatable dinghy which gave hours of enjoyment as I towed them up and down in it or they played with it themselves in shallower waters. There was a need to look out for jelly fish and particularly for the blue 'sails' of the shoals of Portuguese man o' war which occasionally appeared nearby. One of our favourite activities was to build a large, circular fort, complete with moat and castellated with sand pies. It was fortified with cannon balls of sand which were hurled at the incoming tide as it approached and eventually surrounded the fort.

One day we all went out to the reef in a hired dug-out canoe but, apart from greater numbers of brittle star fish and cowrie shells, it was not so different as on the beach itself. The main difference was in the sea near the reef where a wonderful maritime world could be seen with the help of a face mask, snorkel and flippers. I enjoyed snorkelling and swimming around the giant mushroom-shaped coral masses which were the refuge of myriads of fish, including sea horses and snake fish. The scorpion fish, or butterfly fish as it was sometimes called, was quite common near the reef and great care had to be taken not to confuse it with waving strands of seaweed which it closely resembled at times. One afternoon, a fellow guest at 'Whitesands' and I went snorkelling around the reef and he put his hand amongst what he thought was seaweed, only to have it pierced by one of the poisonous spines hidden in the dorsal fins of a scorpion fish. I told him immediately to get into the canoe and paddled back as fast as I could. He was ill within minutes, by the time we had reached the beach he could hardly walk, and he spent three days in Mombasa hospital. Another common fish covered with poisonous spines was the puffer fish; these always turned face on and blew themselves up like footballs. They came close to shore but were readily seen and the children, although warned, regarded them more with amusement than fear. When on the beach, we kept an eye open for attractive pieces of driftwood for Irene to use in flower arrangements. There were also useful-sized pieces of pumice which local people informed us were thought to have originated from the massive eruption of the Pacific island volcano, Krakatoa, which took place in the nineteenth century.

In Easter, 1965, we took local leave in Malindi further up the coast and stayed at the Eden Roc Hotel with Arusha friends, John and Betty Aitkenhead, and their three children Jim, Stuart and Lesley. Linda and Diana and the Aitkenhead children spent hours in and around the swimming pool from which there was a magnificent view of the coastline. There was a squash court very near the hotel and each morning John and I played a few games. I was a bit rusty, not having played it since I was a student, but soon got into the swing of it and greatly enjoyed the brief change from playing tennis in Arusha. Malindi was situated a few miles north of the barrier reef, hence the sand was not the soft white coral sand of Nyali beach, but there were ideal conditions for surfing which the children and I enjoyed. We visited the ancient ruined city of Gedi some eight miles south of Malindi, with its remains of mosque and pillar tombs indicating the presence of an Islamic culture extending back to the twelfth century and trading with distant nations, as shown by a few ornamental blue and white plates still remaining in some of the pillars.

Thereafter, we resumed our holidays at 'Whitesands', Christmas 1966 being notable in that the aircraft carrier *Ark Royal* was in port and the hotel guests hosted the sailors. The following day we were invited back for a drink on board and a tour around the ship which we all enjoyed, including Linda and Diana. Our last visit to 'Whitesands' was in August 1970 by which time, although the original reception area was still present, the old bandas had been replaced by a modern two-storey block of rooms. There was also a modern outdoor swimming pool and dining area. The hotel was taking on the character of an international hotel. While this change was timely and appropriate for the rapidly expanding international tourism of the decade, for us it was losing its magic charm and becoming just another good hotel.

Not only was Arusha an attractive township, but it was also close to the magnificent game reserves of the Ngorongoro crater, Sergengeti plains, Lake Manyara, Momella game park, and Ngurdoto crater. Sometimes, when visitors came from overseas to see the work of the T.P.R.I., it was possible at the weekend to give a day to combining discussions with seeing one of these reserves. I would take them in one of our landrover estate wagons. The drives were almost invariably bumpy and very dusty, but visitors loved seeing the herds of zebra and wildebeest; the not quite so numerous topi, impala, Grant's and Thompson's gazelle; birds such as ostrich, guinea fowl, secretary birds, marabou storks and vultures; and, in the Lake Manyara game reserve, vast numbers of flamingo, pelicans and cormorants. We quite often saw elephant and giant warthog in the Ngurdoto crater. Masai and their settlements, or manyatta, held a fascination for visitors who were intrigued by their simple dwellings; these resembled oval-shaped igloos, about five feet high, constructed of branches and twigs and plastered all over with a mortar made largely of cow dung. We respected nomadic Masai wishes to be left alone and kept a sensible distance away from their manyatta. On one occasion, however, when in the field with my mosquito collectors I was approached by a moran who asked me to come to his manyatta. As we approached, there was a strong smell of cow dung and rancid fat and clouds of house flies. On arrival, we were constantly bitten by stable and horse flies breeding in their outdoor cattle enclosures, or bomas. The old chief appeared, leaning heavily on two strong sticks. Samson Mollel, my Masai staff member, told me that this chief was famous among Masai in this region for his courageous deeds in the past. With great dignity, the chief explained that his dwellings were heavily infested with bed-bugs in such numbers as to be dangerous to 'the men, the cattle and the women'. The beds comprised a 'mattress' made of branches of an extremely prickly shrub, apparently to deter snakes, covered with a well worn sheet of cattle hide. This mattress and the inside walls and roof of the dwellings harboured bed-bugs which were quickly despatched with a single application of insecticide. Several weeks later, Samson presented me with two *rungu* or clubs, one as carried by a moran and the other by a Masai elder.

Arusha was also a splendid centre for mountain climbers, being itself overshadowed by the extinct volcano, Mount Meru, standing at 14,979 feet. It was also only fifty miles or so from the highest mountain in Africa, Kilimanjaro, at well over 19,000 feet, and within a day's drive over the Masai plains to the only active volcano in Tanzania, named Oldyonyo Lengai by the Masai, or 'the Mountain of God'. I climbed Meru three times, the first time in 1960, shortly after arriving in Arusha. This was done one weekend with a few members of the rugby team as a part of our get-fit programme. We commenced the climb at Olmotonyi, entering the forest belt just above the pyrethrum plantations situated a few thousand feet above Arusha. At about twelve thousand feet the forest quickly gave way to almost pure volcanic scree. At this point we camped overnight in the open. We had sleeping bags and maintained a fire built largely from branches of giant heather, but it was intensely cold and we hardly slept. At the first glimmer of light, we set off up the steep, loose scree. The going was quite tiring and it was well past dawn by the time we arrived at the summit, but to the west there was an impressive view of the cloud base, with the enormous pointed shadow of Meru impinged on it and stretching many miles into the distance. To the east of the summit, and only a few feet away from it, there was a sheer drop of thousands of feet where that side of Meru had been blown away in a volcanic eruption that took place long ago, and almost directly below could be seen the mouth of the extinct volcano. It was interesting to note that the snowy peak of Meru, as seen from Arusha in the cool season, was not in fact true snow, but was comprised of consolidated hail or particles of ice. We signed the little book provided at the summit and within an hour returned by giant steps to our camp at the juncture of scree and forest. After a brisk walk through the forest, we reached Olmotonyi in less than four hours and were back in Arusha in time for tea.

A few years later Kay Hocking, his brother, Professor Brian Hocking, and I did the climb. Professor Hocking collected biological specimens on the way up. A year or so later, he published a paper on his findings which included some new records. The climb was made easier by the Mountain Club having built a wooden hut just above the forest edge for climbers to stay in overnight. My last climb was in July 1972, with a party of ten, including three children: these were my younger daughter Diana, then fourteen years old, and her friends, Simon Stephenson and Stephen von Roretz. By this time, Mount Meru featured in tourist brochures and could not be climbed without an official guide. This was arranged, and before the climb I had a meeting at home to check the suitability of the children's climbing clothes, footwear, sleeping gear and provisions, and to ensure that each had a decent alpenstock. The party enjoyed the walk through the forest and I was glad to see that the hut at the top of the forest edge was now a large pre-fabricated aluminium one with windows, and capable of housing our party. We built a fire outdoors and soon had plenty of hot drinks and food available, although, as often on climbs, there were some who did not feel hungry. After a sing-song we retired early to our sleeping bags to be up at first light. Eve and Ian Botham stayed behind to look after the camp, while the rest of us went on to the top, arriving about mid-day. The last thousand feet up the steep, loose scree was quite tiring, and I was glad that the children had heeded my earlier advice which was, when tired, to drive the alpenstock into the scree and sit down for a few minutes with one leg hooked around it, otherwise there was a danger of slipping back. We all signed the book and many had photographs taken of themselves on the summit. While we would have managed without the guide, his presence had been a great asset. He had encouraged the laggards and helped carry their rucksacks when they showed signs of wilting, as well as leading the party when he felt it was required. We returned to the tin hut where Eve and Ian had hot coffee and tea waiting, and then descended through the forest again to the Forest Institute at Olmotonyi, where the guide issued each of us with a nice certificate bearing a picture of Mount Meru and stating that we had climbed the fifth highest mountain in Africa on the 29th day of July 1972.

One day, in the cool dry season of 1962, Dr. Tom Fletcher phoned me from The East African Institute of Malaria at Amani, inviting me to go on a weekend trip with him and his wife, Billah, to climb Oldyonyo Lengai. I accepted at once for, although Lengai was way out in the Masai plains nearly a hundred miles from Arusha, I had every confidence in Tom and Billah as climbing companions, for Tom and I had climbed together as students and Billah was an experienced traveller in East Africa. I also knew the location of Lengai, as it could be seen in the distance to the north from the main Arusha-Babati road whenever I drove to my field station in the Umbugwe area. We set out from my house one Saturday morning, in Tom's short-wheel-based, hard-top landrover, drove down the Babati road, turning off to pass through the village of Mto wa Mbu in the Umbugwe area, and on to Engaruka (Masai for 'the place of the fleas'). From then on, we drove over a mostly trackless plain of wiry yellow grass with a covering of volcanic soil which filled the atmosphere of the vehicle with choking dust, and each time the landrover hit a bump or depression, the windshield was instantly rendered black by a blanket of fine volcanic dust thrown onto it. From time to time, the landrover would also be buffeted by small, but quite powerful, whirlwinds seen to carry pieces of vegetation hundreds of feet into the air. We arrived at the foot of Lengai before dark, pitched tent, and washed off layers of dust using water from jerrycans. After consuming an egg and bacon pie that Irene had provided, we turned in to rise at first light when the sun broke behind the flat-topped, extinct volcano of Ketumbaine which, according to Masai folk-lore, still harboured a few Wambilikimi, or pygmies. Lengai stood out like a school drawing of a volcano – a perfect cone standing nearly 9,000 feet above sea level and 6,000 feet above the Masai plain. It glittered in the dawn light as huge slabs of consolidated ash, intermittently disposed along its sides, gleamed like giant mirrors.

The slopes of Lengai are composed of a series of high ridges, and correspondingly deep gullies, only some of which lead from the bottom to the top. The trick in climbing Lengai is therefore to select a suitable ridge. We selected quite a good one. It was not perfect, because about half way up we came to an arrete about seven feet high which required a bit of surmounting. About two thirds of the way up we left the rather tenacious vegetation zone, including elephant grass, and came on to ridge surfaces composed of consolidated volcanic ash, called 'tuff', and resembling brittle grey concrete. At this point there was a fabulous view. To the south, over 3,000 feet below, lay the pale Masai plain with the faint shadows of clouds passing over it, and scattered deep, black areas where Masai had burnt grass for forcing new growth for their cattle. Also clearly visible in the plain were 'God's footsteps', as Masai called them; these were two huge caldera, one slightly to the front and side of the other, as seen from our position. To the south-east was Mount Ketumbaine, and to the west, in the direction of the rift wall, could be seen twin-coloured Mount Kerimasi, also an extinct volcano. The last third of the climb was steep, but the going was relatively easy on the vegetation-free tuf, although care had to be taken to keep away from brittle cornices of this surface because it alone would not support the weight of a human being.

As we approached the top, we could see a line of baboon sitting around the edge of an old crater which had some grass growing in it, although much of it had been uprooted. We passed a magnificent dome-shaped volcanic plug and thereafter soon reached the summit with its large cairn of stones, among which was concealed an old oval-shaped chocolate tin holding the inevitable note-book. After signing the book, we replaced it in the tin, taking great care to return it securely among the cairn. The crater was most impressive, with its steep walls white with ash and pierced with steaming fumaroles, and the floor of the crater, although largely inactive, had several small splatter cones discharging sulphurous fumes and a slow stream of lava reminiscent of blackcurrant jam. The view to the north from the summit was very different from that to the south, but equally impressive for much of Lake Natron could be seen, its entire edge appearing as a wide white band due to the presence of vast quantities of the salt-soda complex, known locally as 'magadi', and derived from volcanic activity. To the east of Lake Natron could be seen another extinct volcano, Mount Gelai. After about half an hour's rest, we commenced our descent along the route of ascent and reached base camp in the early afternoon, thus giving us enough time to return to Arusha the same day. We returned by a different route, heading north past Mount Gelai and towards Mount Longido, in due course bringing us onto the main Arusha–Nairobi road and home shortly after dark. It had been an exciting safari but it must have been nothing in comparison with that of Professor Fritz Jaeger who, in 1906, was the first European to climb Lengai and enter its crater.

At T.P.R.I. there had been talk in the staff room for some time about organizing an expedition up Kilimanjaro. In July 1963, this became reality when six of us, George Burnett, Kay Hocking, Cliff Lee, Jacobai Morar, David Webley and myself, did the climb. The weather was perfect, and we set out from Kibo Hotel where the proprietress, Mrs Bruehl, provided the guide and porters. There had been considerable changes since my previous climb in 1952. The hotel had a large, modern, two-storey wing and there was a rough motor track through the forest to the first mountain hut situated 12,000 feet up at the top of the forest line. This mountain hut, which has been called the Kilimanjaro rest house before Tanganyika's independence in 1961, was now renamed the Mandara rest house. Kay took the rucksacks and one or two climbers and porters up in his landrover, so that the camp was well established by the time the walkers had arrived. Several others and I went on foot to enjoy aspects of the forest environment, such as the lovely curtains of lichens among the branches, and also with the idea that the walk might help us to acclimatize to mountain conditions. The Mandara hut was essentially the same building as before but with extensive renovations. Its window shutters were immaculate and its whitewashed walls gleamed in the sun. The second day provided a glorious walk through the mainly grassy zone above the forest line, with the twin peaks of Kibo and Mawenzi standing out sharply in the clear mountain air. The second mountain hut, at 14,000 feet, previously called Peter's hut, had been renamed the Mawenzi hut. The hut was now in better repair and bigger, having been extended by the addition of a larger building, also clad in aluminium sheeting. The guide produced a generous meal which, par for the course, was largely eaten by himself and the porters, as some of the climbers had lost their appetites and were sustaining themselves almost entirely on boiled sweets and tea or water.

On the third day, we went up to the saddle between Kibo and Mwenzi. The terrain was almost free of vegetation, but progress was nevertheless slow due to the discomforting effects of high altitude and of icy piercing winds crossing the saddle. After a stop on the saddle to drink hot tea from vacuum flasks, we proceeded on to Kibo hut situated at the foot of Mount Kibo at 16,000 feet. I could not detect any major change in the building since my last visit but it was in a much better state of repair and without gaps through which the wind could freely enter. We arose in the early hours of the fourth day and, in the dim light of a lamp held by the guide, ascended the steep scree slope of Kibo, pausing every three steps or so to recuperate. We all made Gilman's Point on the rim of the outer crater and, while my friends and colleagues rested and enjoyed the spectacular view emerging in the rays of the rising sun, I pressed on with the guide in a determined effort to reach the summit, called the Kaiser Willhelm Spitz before Tanganyika's independence in 1961, and since then renamed Uhuru Point. The journey around the outer rim to Uhuru Point was absolutely exhausting due to the rarefied air at that altitude and the effort required to maintain balance on the bizarre snow formations under foot. These took the form of snow shaped by high winds into stepping stones, each about three feet long and a foot or so wide, three feet high and a foot or so apart. It was a relief to arrive at the summit, which was free from snow. The guide and I took photographs and I signed the book which was quite a large one and contained in a proper metal mountain box. I was very pleased to have made it for, apart from the sense of achievement experienced in getting there, there were incredible views of the inner crater, the ice-stone in the outer crater, and walls of ice curtains around the outer crater.

After a few minutes rest, the guide and I returned to Gilman's Point to meet my T.P.R.I. friends who had enjoyed their hour's rest in the sun during my absence and were ready to face the descent. The difference between ascending and descending was like chalk and cheese for we hurtled back down the scree, the only restriction being the willingness of the knees to take the strain. We crossed the saddle at a fair speed and reached Mawenzi mountain hut mid-afternoon. While we were resting, washing and patching blisters, the guide and porters picked everlasting flowers and made them into simple crowns for each of us as a mark of our success. Mine had additional bits sticking out to indicate that I had reached the summit. We arose early on the fifth day and walked down to the Mandara hut, from where some continued on foot and others in Kay's landrover. On reaching Kibo Hotel, we had a cold beer and a light meal and, after declaring the climb a success, returned by road to Arusha the same day.

The 1960s were politically exciting times in East Africa in which I became increasingly involved, not through any deliberate effort on my part, but through a chain of events arising from the determination of the East African countries to achieve independence from colonial rule. Tanganyika already had a strong political party, the Tanganyika African National Union, established in 1954 to fight for independence by peaceful means. Its leader, Mwalimu Julius Nyerere, was much respected, not only by Africans but also by the British government, which granted Tanganyika internal self-government, or 'ushirika', in September 1960. At this time I had many African staff under my charge, and we worked in somewhat remote villages. It was thus possible to hear the views of 'watu wa kanuni', or common people, particularly at the end of a day's work when relationships were less formal. They were remarkably relaxed in manner and in no way aggressive, but simply wanted their freedom, or 'uhuru'. All of them, old or young, had, within living memory, been born under colonial rule, be it German or British. They were not overtly concerned about pragmatic matters, as to how the country was going to make a success of this or that after independence. A number of expatriates were, however, justifiably concerned, particularly farmers and members of the business community. Colonial servants, on pensionable terms, had less cause for concern as they had the prospect of a generous 'golden handshake' and pension payable in the United Kingdom. Following 'ushirika', the normally ubiquitous greeting of 'Hujambo' was often followed by the expression 'Uhuru na Umoja' – Freedom (Independence) and Unity. Sometimes the latter expression was replaced by the gesture of raising the forefinger of the right hand. At other times the expression used was 'Uhuru na kazi' – Freedom and work – to show recognition that freedom carried with it the responsibility of a great deal of work.

On 16th October 1961, Tanganyika gained full independence, which was celebrated throughout the country by dignified ceremonies in which the Union Jack was lowered and the green, black and gold flag of Tanganyika raised immediately after midnight. Independence was also celebrated in December 1961 by a symbolic torch of freedom which was lit in Dar-es-Salaam and carried by a Tanganyikan athlete to the summit of Kilimanjaro, thereafter named Uhuru Point. In December 1962, Tanganyika was declared a republic with Julius Nyerere as President. In January 1964, Tanganyika merged with Zanzibar to form the Republic of Tanzania, following a revolution in Zanzibar against its Sultan-led, Arab-dominated government. The merger was reflected in the Tanzanian national flag which included a patch of blue in recognition of the new country spanning the sea.

The Tropical Pesticides Research Institute was quite considerably affected by Tanganyika's independence. Before independence, it was called the Colonial Insecticides Research Unit and was a Tanganyika government research station, with Kay Hocking as officer-in-charge, answerable to the Colonial Pesticides Committee in the U.K. In April 1961, its name was changed to the Tropical

Pesticides Research Institute, and in the following July, Kay Hocking was appointed Director and George Burnett Deputy Director. On 1st July 1962, the Institute changed from a Tanganyika research organization into one of twelve research organizations of the East African Common Services Organization, which had its headquarters in Nairobi. The East African Common Services Organization had previously been the East African High Commission, but this change followed independence of Kenya and Uganda in 1962.

The above changes affected all staff regarding conditions of service, including pensionable expatriate staff of the Institute who with effect from 1 July 1962 became eligible for East African Common Services compensation and retirement benefits. These changes were achieved over many months, during which there was much speculation in the Institute's staff room and a little too much hounding of Kay Hocking for details which he was in no position to provide. In due course all entitled officers, including myself, received a twelve-page copy of the scheme of compensation and retirement benefits applicable to staff members of the East African Common Services Organization. In essence, the scheme applied to officers, confirmed in their posts and under fifty-five years old. They would receive compensation for loss of career if they volunteered to take early retirement or if they were compulsorily retired under the East African Common Services Africanization Programme. The maximum compensation was £12,000 for those who had completed at least ten years of pensionable service. In addition, the retiring officers would immediately receive a pension relating to length of pensionable service. The pension would also be favourable in so far as it would be based on pensionable emoluments at the date of retirement and not on 'averaging' of pensionable emoluments over a number of years, which was the normal basis for calculation of pensions. The scheme was quite ingenious for, while it offered generous compensation for those who retired immediately, it also offered considerable incentives for officers to stay on. It seemed that the designers of the scheme had taken into account the consequences of earlier compensation schemes in other countries which had encouraged entitled officers to retire straight away. In these earlier schemes, while the ensuing

137

mass exodus of colonial officers had given a measure of political satisfaction, a year or so later it became apparent that too much expertise had been lost, and considerable overseas recruitment on contract terms had to be carried out, with salaries offered far exceeding those of the previous pensionable incumbents.

One incentive in the East African Common Services Scheme was that compensation was to be paid over a period of five years in six instalments, recalculated each year to take the additional service into account, interest to be paid annually at five per cent per annum on the outstanding balance of compensation due. However, if an officer reached fifty-five before receiving the six instalments, he then received no further instalments but was immediately given the balance of compensation due to him. Another incentive related to the pension for, in addition to the normal entitlement to commute one-quarter of the pension, a further sixteenth could be commuted for each year after the scheme became operational on 1st July 1962. In the case of officers serving under the oversea superannuation scheme, of whom I was one, there were slight differences in pension entitlements. In addition to a lump sum given with a smaller pension, one twelfth of the pension could be assigned as a gratuity for each year after the operative date. Also, the pension was based on the average of pensionable emoluments received over the last three years of service.

The scheme received much discussion in the staff room, as the ten or so entitled expatriate officers evaluated their position with regard to possible africanization or the best time to retire voluntarily. There were also more than a dozen expatriate staff employed on two or three year contracts equally prone to africanization, which could be implemented immediately following completion of contract and without compensation. A few of the contract staff disapproved of the compensation scheme, in particular one officer who, some years earlier, had turned down the offer to convert from contract terms to pensionable employment because he had considered contract gratuities more remunerative than pensions. The scheme worked well, allowing africanization to proceed at a slow pace as appropriate for a research institute requiring quite a number of professionally qualified staff. Non-graduate expatriate staff, primarily laboratory technicians and field officers, were the first to be africanized and, apart from a few vacancies, this was achieved in 1966. It was extremely difficult to obtain African research officers for, of eight recruited in 1966, two were African and six were expatriate staff on contract terms. In October 1966, Kay Hocking left on retirement leave and I was the only entitled officer remaining on the staff.

In the 1960s, with world attention on developing countries as many more achieved independence, they were given strong international support, and bilateral efforts were made by several countries, including the United Kingdom, to improve the health and well-being of peoples in developing countries through eradication or control of diseases such as malaria and onchocerciasis, and control of pests that devastated food and cash crops. The main means of control were through the use of pesticides, chiefly insecticides, but also including fungicides and herbicides; and undoubtedly these pesticides assisted in saving millions of lives and improved the living standards of millions of people during this decade. The Tropical Pesticides Research Institute was very active and was widely perceived as doing valuable work, not only for East Africa but also, as a designated WHO Collaborating Laboratory, for developing countries as a whole. I was able to get lots of research done, and in 1965, at the relatively early age of thirty-eight, the University of Birmingham awarded me the degree of Doctor of Science on my published work. In retrospect, I regret not taking time off and sparing the money to fly to the U.K. to attend the award ceremony, meet old colleagues, and receive a proper illuminated certificate. As it was, I received a small and extremely unpretentious certificate by air mail. I had probably then considered the time and money better spent on a local leave at Mombasa. Following independence, promotion also went ahead quite fast, for I rose from Senior Scientific Officer in 1962 to Acting Director in October 1966, and was confirmed as Director on 1st April 1967.

I went on six weeks home leave between August and October 1966, the leave being a short one to fit in with taking over from Kay Hocking. My family and I travelled by air in conformity with government passage entitlements, which had been changed following improvements in air travel and the cessation of government servants' normal entitlement to sea passages. The flight from Arusha to Nairobi was in an old DC3, but that from Nairobi to Heathrow was our first one in a jet plane, a VC10. One of our main objectives on home leave was to equip and introduce our children into Ashford School as boarders. When planning where to spend leave in the U.K., I took into account our wish to stay at a seaside resort, and be within easy reach of Ashford school and Irene's brother's home at Burgess Hill. Accordingly, I took a map and ruled a straight line between Ashford and Burgess Hill and, using this line as the base, drew a more or less equilateral triangle with the apex on the coast. This indicated a resort in East Sussex, unfamiliar to us, named Bexhill-on-Sea. We enjoyed the leave in Bexhill but were a little unhappy when putting the children into boarding school. There were many houses for sale at this time and we inspected some but, as we could not find an estate agent interested in managing property in our absence overseas, we did not pursue the matter further.

Kay handed over directorship of the Institute to me within a fortnight of my return from home leave, and the day before he went on retirement leave. His view, which in a very short time also became my own, was that one could only really learn how to direct through actually being in that post. He was a great loss to the Institute and Arusha, in which he had been very active socially, particularly in tennis, golf and amateur theatricals.

The Tropical Pesticides Research Institute was one of the largest research institutes in East Africa, having 135 staff in 1966. This establishment comprised director, deputy director, 15 research officers, 1 pilot, 1 senior executive officer, 1 accounts officer, 3 laboratory technicians, 3 laboratory technician trainees, 1 senior field officer, 8 field officers, 2 assistant field officers, 1 personal secretary, 1 storekeeper, 6 clerical officers, 2 works overseers, 1 artisan foreman, 14 laboratory assistants, 11 technical assistants, 5 drivers, 1 works foreman and 56 subordinate staff. Headquarters were on its 25-acre site at Mringa and included: 1 administrative block, 9 laboratories, 1 hospital dispensary, 1 animal house, 3 greenhouses, 1 workshop block, 1 store block and 43 houses for junior staff. 22 houses for senior staff were located in Arusha Township, and a further seven in field stations. T.P.R.I. also had a light aircraft – a Cessna 182 – and aircraft hangar at Arusha airport, and 20 motor vehicles. The director was also warrant holder and responsible for financial management of the Institute's annual budget in excess of three million East African shillings, then equivalent to £150,000. For the following three years, I was never so busy in my life but this seemed to create a capacity for doing more in a day than I would have thought possible. There appeared to be some truth in the remark once made to me that 'if you want something done, ask someone who is busy'.

I enjoyed the mental stimulation of having to think and talk about other research programmes as well as those in my own field, for I was now in charge of the overall scientific programme of the Institute which included research in agricultural and medical entomology, molluscicides and bilharzia, herbicides, fungicides and plant pathology, chemistry, physics and engineering. For several months I had difficulty in remembering the technical names, trade names or code numbers of the considerable number of compounds involved, particularly herbicides. In agricultural research, I was helped by Ephata Materu whose subject was agricultural entomology and who was now Deputy Director. The research staff, most of whom were expatriates on contract terms, naturally wanted to get as much good work done as possible since they never knew whether or not their posts would be africanized at the end of a tour. The African research staff were also interested in getting higher degrees such as Ph.D and so they, too, were motivated to get a lot done.

There were tremendous budget constraints with annual increases more or less linked to normal salary increments, but in no way providing for the enormous increases in costs of imported laboratory materials and equipment. Additional budgetary constraints arose from the British government gradually replacing its automatic counterpart contribution of fifty per cent to the East African Common Services annual budget by project-funding. The basis of the project approach was that the U.K. reviewed research proposals offered by the East African Common Services, selected those which it wished to support, and provided counterpart funding sometimes far exceeding fifty per cent of the overall cost. This approach had a great deal to commend it, not only from the technical point of view but also from that of financial accountability. It did, however, mean that less funds were available for *virement* to cover any overspending that might occur under permitted sub-heads. From the beginning, I supported the work of the research staff as much as possible, but had constantly to refer to the Institute's vote book and watch expenditure like a hawk. In this way I was always able to keep within the overall budget, although sometimes by a very small margin. With the rapid changes of staff at senior level in the East African community taking place concurrently with a major change in overseas funding, some other departments within the community apparently experienced even greater difficulty in maintaining financial control, for I twice received cables from headquarters to 'quote savings' from my budget for *virement* to another department or institute, and once, in headquarters, heard an official lamenting that he had 'not overspent, but merely underestimated'.

After Kenya, Tanganyika and Uganda had become independent, the three countries wished to strengthen their ties but perceived that their common services, first under the East African High Commission, and then under the East African Common Services Organization, were unequally shared and far too much to the benefit of Kenya. The East African Community thus evolved, bringing with it relocation of its headquarters from Nairobi to Arusha, and intentions for re-siting its twelve research institutes as necessary. There was a formal establishment of the East African Community by 'The Authority' (i.e. the three heads of state) in Arusha on 1st December 1967 and a reception by them afterwards, held in the Arusha School. There was an impressive gathering of heads of state of many African countries, ministers from Kenya, Tanganyika and Uganda, and other senior officials, including directors of institutes. President Kenyatta, Nyerere and Obote sat together at a table and received congratulations from guests filing past, including myself. In Arusha township itself, there was much public warmth and well being, and frequent raising of three fingers to indicate a desire for 'shirikisho', or federation, of the three countries.

The relocation from Nairobi to Arusha involved about three hundred staff and had a tremendous impact on Arusha. There was a major problem in finding suitable office accommodation and housing for staff. The civic centre, the largest administrative building in Arusha, was made available by the Tanzanian government to accommodate the office of the Secretary General, and private houses and shops near the civic centre were converted for temporary use by The Community Service Commission and Tanzania Government. Offices and housing at the Government Agricultural Training Centre at Tengeru, some seven miles from Arusha, were made available to the East African Community Finance and Administrative Secretariat, including the Supplies Branch and Works Division. The twenty-two houses in Arusha township belonging to my own institute were of a high standard and envious eyes were cast on them by many of the new arrivals from Nairobi. There were periodical proposals that the T.P.R.I. houses should be included within an East African Community housing pool but these never matured. However, although T.P.R.I. managed to retain its own houses for accommodation of its staff, maintenance of the T.P.R.I. houses and its other buildings passed to the East African Community Works and Estate Management Division, based at Tengeru.

The first house to receive redecoration under this new arrangement was a lovely bungalow. A works foreman, enthusiastic to change the earlier colonial practice of applying only cream paint to walls indoors and outdoors, painted them in the Tanzanian national colours of deep blue, gold, green and black. The bungalow was then occupied by Peter Ward on his arrival as head of a tropical bird pest control project based at T.P.R.I. He was admirably unperturbed by the colour scheme and in a few weeks had repainted it more to his taste, which included mostly cream. Shortly afterwards, the works division issued a short list of colours from which a choice could be made for house redecoration by its staff. This arrangement proved most satisfactory, and within a year this division expanded and developed into a most efficient arm of the East African Community.

The arrival in Arusha of highly educated Kenyan and Ugandan staff members of the East African Community, as well as Tanzanian ones, had a moderating influence on the lifestyle and public attitudes of the Arusha community. Several joined the

143

Arusha Gymkhana Club and took a most active part in tennis, golf and other social events, thereby helping to dispel concern by some members of the public that the club was an outmoded enclave of colonialism and should be disbanded, as had some clubs in other parts of the country. There was also a more tolerant attitude to the way people dressed in public, for most of the Kenyan and Ugandan men preferred to wear European-style suits during working hours rather than colourful smock-type shirts, Kaunda-style suits, or the flowing robes of national dress of many Tanzanian staff. A quite attractive 'Mother Hubbard' style of long dress was adopted by many Tanzanian women and was sometimes worn by other nationalities, including Europeans. There was, however, a severe crackdown on mini-skirts which were widely in fashion in 1967 and sometimes worn by African wives of staff members of the East African Community, as well as European ones. All women in Arusha wearing dresses or skirts above knee level were liable to be challenged by 'Green Guards' – vigilant members of the Tanzanian Youth Organization – and accused of insulting the nation. However, within a few months, the 'Green Guards' became more aware of the international character of Arusha society and, with the exception of mini-skirts, were most tolerant of the variety of dress worn by women in Arusha.

Since I was concerned with control of pests of medical and agricultural importance, I attended annual meetings of the East African National Resources Research Council and the East African Medical Research Council. In addition, I was a member of the Agricultural Research Coordinating Committee and the Forestry Research Coordinating Committee, both of which also met annually. Through these meetings I enjoyed lively discussions with fellow directors of the other eleven research institutes under the aegis of the East African Community, and with ministers, distinguished doctors and scientists working in East Africa. I also met eminent United Kingdom members of the research councils who flew out to attend these meetings and take the opportunity to visit several of the research institutes and see some of the work being done in the laboratory and in the field. The first meeting that I attended was the Natural Resources Research Council under the extremely able and experienced chairmanship of Chief Adam Sapi

Mkwawa, OBE, and the following two coordinating committees were chaired by Lord Portsmouth of equal calibre. A year later, I had acquired a much greater understanding of agriculture-related activities and, having grown into the post of Director, was able to present my reports with a great deal more confidence than in the previous year. Also, by then, less space was given to great technical detail in reports because of the committee's greater concern with determining research priorities and avoiding duplication in research in view of prevailing financial restrictions and the East African Community's proposal to re-site research institutes to provide more equitable services within the three countries. Institute reports also had to present proposals for research projects under the new funding arrangements and inform the meetings of progress with africanization and training, and these subjects took up further time in discussion. I always enjoyed presenting reports at meetings of the East African Medical Research Council, as medical entomology was my own subject area. Most meetings that I attended were chaired by the Vice-chairman, Mr. A. Michael Wood, the famous 'flying doctor' of East Africa, and Director of the African and Medical Research Foundation in Nairobi.

Preparing annual reports for two councils, two coordinating committees, and the Institute was time-consuming enough but, in addition to these, there was a constant demand from the Research and Social Council for reports giving information to assist its deliberations on re-siting research institutes. In this context, T.P.R.I. was in a pivotal position because much of its work was concerned with the same important vectors and pests as those receiving study by several other East African Community research institutes and national research organizations. As these latter reports were frequently required as a matter of urgency, through necessity I became skilful in rapidly producing reports, often facilitated by judicious use of scissors and paper-stapler. Our cyclostyling machine was constantly churning out numerous copies and bundles of them, wrapped in pink ribbon, were despatched to the secretary of the responsible council or committee. After the East African Community headquarters had moved to Arusha, with some offices located in Tengeru, some of these bundles would go astray. At first, when this happened, I had another set of copies made from the original stencil, which was kept in reserve for possible occasions such as this, and delivered them myself. Later on, I simply delivered the bundle of reports myself to the secretary's office, but even then replacements were sometimes necessary. It seemed that the temporary office accommodation and facilities at Tengeru had difficulty in physically coping with the vast quantities of documents required by the councils.

Appropriately enough, in early 1967, newspapers and East African Community information circulars frequently carried articles such as 'The Community is on the Move'. Indeed it was, and the spirit of urgency was reflected in the speed with which some staff members drove between Nairobi and Arusha. There were many car accidents with injuries to, and even the death of, some senior personnel. There were also quite a number of private car accidents among staff of my own institute, particularly those in the recently africanized posts of field officers, whose terms of employment included entitlement to a car-loan. However, within a year or two the number of accidents greatly diminished as the owners became more careful drivers and experienced the heavy personal costs of car repair. About this time there was a revival of interest in an old topic of placing one's fate in the hands of the official driver, for in the East African Community, as in many government departments, an official vehicle could only be driven by an African specifically appointed on the staff as driver or driver/mechanic. This led to the better drivers in the Institute being far more sought after than the others, and a need for passengers to exercise great restraint in their comments at hazardous moments. Reflex outbursts by an expatriate, such as 'You idiot!', could be sufficient grounds for almost instant repatriation. On these occasions, Swahili expressions such as 'enesha kwa utaratibu!' ('drive with care') or 'haraka, haraka haina baraka' ('hurry, hurry has no blessing') were useful and without offence. Sometimes a driver would disconcertingly reply 'Inshallah' ('it is in the hands of God'). Although regulations provided for dismissal of bad drivers, I recall very few instances of any being dismissed, and during twenty-two years of having official drivers in East Africa, I was involved in many near misses but never in a serious accident in which I was a passenger with an official driver.

146

Within two years of the East African Community headquarters move to Arusha, all field officer posts and five scientific officer posts at T.P.R.I. had been africanized and two African trainee scientific officers had been appointed. These achievements were largely due to the energetic africanization policy pursued by the East African Community Service Commission, which frequently advertised vacancies in the overseas press as well as in local newspapers. For several months, following a spate of rapid africanization, two bachelor African graduates, one Kenyan and the other Ugandan, had to share one of T.R.P.I.'s houses in Arusha township. Although the house was a nice one with three bedrooms and plenty of space, they just could not get along with each other. They would frequently visit me in turn and complain about the other's domestic lifestyle. I understood their position and was most sympathetic about it, for they were in a foreign country, of different nationality, and away from close relations which play such an important part in African domestic life. I subsequently learnt from other members of the East African Community that this type of problem was not unique to T.P.R.I., and I was probably not alone in bringing it to the attention of the Community Service Commission which was based in Arusha. Shortly afterwards, staff recruitment took into account the availability of housing as well as vacant posts.

T.P.R.I. had an active training programme much encouraged by the Community Service Commission. There was in-service training whereby a newly graduated trainee research officer was attached to work with an experienced research officer for two years. Laboratory technicians were first sent to Uganda Technical College in Kampala to train for their City and Guilds examination, but this course was changed to day release, and they then had to go to the Tropical Products Institute in London for further training. The Community Service Commission found it necessary to 'bond' staff going overseas for training, since after a year or two in the U.K. or America some were reluctant to return. I received several letters from one laboratory technician, training in the U.K., who wanted to stay on to take a degree so that he could 'build the nation with my head and not just with my hands'. In the late 1960s, quite a number of East Africans were sent to the Martinovsky Institute in Moscow for post-graduate training. One of T.P.R.I.'s physicists had received this training but his appointment at the appropriate step in the scientific officer's salary scale was not easy to determine, for the Russian qualification did not quite correspond to a Ph.D., nor had he two years of post-graduate research behind him prior to his appointment.

Although great efforts were made to africanize research officer posts, it was extremely difficult to fill all the posts with properly-qualified Africans, and so the Community Service Commission agreed to the appointment of expatriates when no suitable African candidate could be obtained. Most of these appointments at T.P.R.I. took place between 1966 and 1969, and with British personnel. This period corresponded to a time of great social change in the U.K. The Beatles were at their zenith, long hair among men was in fashion, and there was a tremendous sense of freedom and tolerance in styles of living. Old colonial attitudes were most definitely rejected. I went to meet one young, newly-appointed entomologist when he arrived at Arusha airport. He was tall, with hair extending down his shoulders, and was dressed casually in jeans and coloured shirt, and had a tendency to nod and say 'Yeah, yeah'. After greeting and welcoming him, I jokingly enquired if he had brought a guitar. He replied that he had brought two, but one had been badly damaged in transit. After about a year, he married the Institute's plant pathologist, who was a Hollander of Surinamese extraction, and they are still happily married. I enjoyed discussion and banter with this new generation of expatriates, being a great believer in the academic and social value of the coffee-break, which was held in the library each morning. In the early months after their arrival, as well as being interested in their own research work, they seemed far more interested in the work of their colleagues than I remember being at the same age. Indeed, so great was their interest in the work of the Institute that they requested a fortnightly meeting of research staff so that they could keep in touch with each others' work. I arranged this and the meetings were a great success for about six months, after which their interest declined, and the meetings even became construed as a waste of time by those who were so involved with their own research programmes that they resented giving up valuable time to hear details of other people's work. There was a general sigh of relief when I reduced these meetings to the previous rate of once every quarter or half year, which was usually quite sufficient for programme planning.

Many of my African colleagues were intrigued by post-colonial expatriates and had mixed feelings about them. Their absence of a colonial past, and their great efforts to talk to Africans of every cadre more like social equals, were strongly in their favour. Sometimes, however, their concern for equality was carried further than Africans wanted. Expatriates dressed in national-type costume were tolerated, but a few caused unspoken embarrassment when, without any knowledge of their customs or language, they tried to identify with Africans by joining in a tribal activity such as a dance. I was aware of very few instances of this in Arusha, but one of my Ugandan colleagues told me that, while there was a great respect for the activities of the Peace Corps in Uganda, one or two Africans referred to them as the 'Pest Corps' because of misplaced social efforts by a few members. This was not a problem at T.R.P.I., but there were one or two occasions when African colleagues or junior staff-members working for post-colonial expatriates did not come up to the expatriates' expectations in work-performance, in spite of comprehensive and courteous conversations in English, or translation into Swahili by an intermediary when appropriate. In some instances there was a communication problem, but it seemed to me that the main difficulty was that, even though they often had theoretical justification on their side, post-colonial expatriates sometimes expected too much from their African colleagues whose qualifications had been achieved against an immensely more difficult background than themselves. In general, African staff preferred an expatriate who was pleasant and respectful but unobtrusive and, where appropriate, prepared him in as short time as possible for taking over his post.

There was also a gradual change in type of visiting expert from Britain. Once I had overcome some slight nervousness and awe of them in general, I found that, with regard to guidance in research, the most valuable and interesting visitors were the most senior ones who either had years of field experience behind them or, who, through high academic positions, had been closely involved in tropical disease or agricultural research over many years. They could readily relate to the technical problems and working conditions of people working in out-stations. Discussions with them were very largely about research in progress or planned, and without great emphasis on completion times or financial aspects, although of course these existed and were spoken about. I took great pains to ensure that the research staff had good opportunities at work to meet these distinguished visitors. Irene and I also held drinks parties at home for overseas visitors to meet research staff socially. On these occasions, Linda and Diana were sometimes allowed to peep round a door to see the arrival of 'the old men'. Among these most welcome visitors from the U.K. were Dr. P.W. Dill-Russell, Dr. L.G. Goodwin, Dr. C.E. Gordon Smith, Dr. J.B. Gray, Dr. Brandon S. Lush, Professors G. Macdonald and A.M. Woodruff (who were concerned with the control of tropical diseases), and Professors A. Robertson and R.L. Wain (who were members of the East African Natural Resources Research Council).

As research funding started to move away from a large but simple financial counterpart contribution by the U.K. to the East African Community budget, and towards the funding of specific projects, a new type of distinguished visitor came to T.P.R.I. from the U.K. They were generally a little younger and without an obvious colonial background, but extremely able and dynamic and very much concerned with getting research on a new footing. This meant that much of the discussion about research was related to drafting project proposals, including proposed personnel to be seconded from the U.K. or employed specifically for the project, African counterpart staff, and the separate contributions of the U.K. and the East African Community in terms of finance, housing vehicles and travel. Dr. Peter Haskell, Director of the U.K. Ministry of Overseas Development Centre for Overseas Pest Research, visited the Institute, and over a period of several months we draughted a project proposal for the control of tropical bird-pests in East Africa. I presented this to the E.A. Natural Research Council as part of T.P.R.I.'s planned research programme for 1968, and it was accepted and duly implemented with success. Draughting of a herbicide project began in the same year with the help of Dr. R.K. Cunningham of the Ministry of Overseas Development, and in cooperation with Mr. J. Fryer, Director of the

U.K. Agricultural Research Council Weed Research Organization. There had developed a certain initial unease among some senior officials of the East African Community about the project approach in general, possibly because of curtailment in use of funds, the reappearance of expatriates on Institute staff, and a sense of incomplete control over research programmes. These fears appeared to evaporate, and the proposed herbicide project was accepted by the Natural Resources Research Council and implemented two years later.

Day to day life in post-independent Tanzania was never boring. Unexpected tragi-comic incidents frequently occurred and the following are a few examples. An American colleague, accompanying me into Arusha Post Office, without any intention of being impolite, addressed an African post office official as 'Buster'. He was immediately accused of calling him a 'bastard', and had an uncomfortable few minutes avoiding being expelled from the country. With rapid africanization taking place at senior levels, there were, quite understandably, a few Africans who were not fully familiar with English idioms and who were unaware of the convention at 'Cocktails' of normally taking only one or two fingers of spirits per glass, and not half a glass or more at any one time. Drinks parties therefore sometimes took an unexpected turn. On one occasion, Irene and I attended a formal evening held by the East African Community at the old East African High Commission Building in Nairobi; this was retained by the East African Community and accommodated a number of its departments. There was an atmosphere of great dignity, and towards the end of the evening Irene was courteously asked by an African guest, wearing a magnificent sash across his chest, it she would like 'one for the bed'. His companion quickly indicated that the correct expression was 'one for the road'. The ensashed gentleman instantly apologised and passed out, falling over Irene's foot and trapping it to the floor, causing the companion to murmur 'Most inappropriate!'.

In January 1971, General Idi Amin seized power in Uganda while President Obote was out of the country. President Nyerere was outraged and in the following year made covert attempts to overthrow him. My own awareness of this arose one night at the

Arusha Gymkhana Club when army personnel appeared bristling with guns and questioning members as to their whereabouts the previous evening, particularly in relation to the new Kilimanjaro international airport. A rumour then rapidly circulated around town that an aircraft had attempted to land at the airport late at night to pick up soldiers as part of a plan to invade Uganda. Because lights for landing and take-off had not yet been installed, the aircraft severely damaged its undercarriage on landing and could not take off with the troops. Some justification for this rumour arose soon afterwards at a research council meeting in which I was present. A member from Kenya inquired as to who was going to bear the cost of recent damage to an aircraft of the East African Community that had been used by the Tanzania Government apparently without Community consent. No short answer was provided and this matter was still under debate when I left the country on retirement later in the year.

Shortly after the airport incident, local government was highly active looking for spies 'within and without'. One day during this period, when Irene and I were in our car, parked outside a shop, waiting for a few minutes to pick up our friend, Abbas Moledina, for a game of tennis, a police landrover came alongside and an officer asked me what I was doing. He was not satisfied with my explanation, jumped out of his landrover, and thrust his rifle alternately in the face of Irene and in mine, and ordered me to drive into the police compound. In the inspector's office, Irene and I received a ritual speech about colonials and colonialism, and I was also interrogated in detail about where I lived and worked. I replied at some length, in Swahili, mentioning a few things such as that my wife had recently been teaching two of President Nyerere's children at Arusha School, whereupon his manner changed and he expressed a great interest in the work of the T.P.R.I. and an eagerness to work there under my direction. We parted on most affable terms, particularly when I indicated that Arusha police might perhaps one day beat T.P.R.I. at soccer.

Shortly after taking over as Director of T.P.R.I., I became aware that there was a staff union, with clerical officer George Kitta, its active and most capable secretary. Three or four members representing the union, and an equal number from management

152

(usually comprising Ephata Materu, John Parker and myself) gathered in the library once a month. At the first meeting I encouraged those present to sit at random around the table and took the attitude that we were all there simply as a group brought together to discuss and resolve problems. This approach did not work at all well, for I soon realized that what the union wanted was a staff versus management situation, with the Director granting them their requests through hard negotiation if necessary. At the next meeting the management, with me in the chair, sat at one end of the table and the union representatives at the other end. Although the union representatives were quite aggressive at times, and I let off steam once or twice, this arrangement worked very well and relations outside the meeting remained not only cordial, but were even improved. Africanization, terms of service, and salary scales featured prominently in most meetings but some business also centred round the T.P.R.I. soccer team, transport for junior staff, and more drugs and equipment for the T.P.R.I. dispensary. As in many countries, soccer was an extremely popular sport in Tanzania. T.P.R.I. junior staff had a good team but insufficient funds to buy a new football and jerseys, so, after considering a request from the union for their purchase from Institute funds, I agreed to pay for a ball from petty cash but not the jerseys. Instead, I sent a circular around all staff explaining the team's situation and enough money was raised by voluntary contributions to buy the jerseys. With the arrival of the East African Headquarters in Arusha, transport between T.P.R.I. and Arusha seven miles away became more frequent and involved more personnel, so, after taking into account comments by the staff union and at John Parker's suggestion, I purchased two new Ford transit buses for our vehicle fleet, whose passenger vehicles comprised largely landrovers and an old single decker bus which had become too heavy on petrol to be used more than occasionally. The transit buses were greatly appreciated by all staff and were the envy of other departments of the community in Arusha, particularly those whose members had to frequently travel the ten miles or so between Tengeru and Arusha.

The Institute had a small dispensary on site for use by staff, wives and children of junior staff who lived in the forty-three

T.P.R.I. houses there. It was supplied with simple dressings, aspirins and anti-malaria tablets made available, as required, by a T.P.R.I. laboratory technician living on the site and who was treated with respect by many of the junior staff and, I sensed, also with a tinge of fear. When, at one meeting, the staff union requested expansion of the dispensary so that room could be made available for a bed for examination of patients, I declined and asked Dr. David Brooke, the Regional Medical Officer, to visit the first aid post and give guidance and, if necessary, direction on its usage. After looking at the attendance register and enquiring about supplies and equipment, he asked the technician why he wanted a bed in the building. The technician launched forth on its facilitating proper examination of patients and in the same breath also asked for a stethoscope. He explained that it would be useful in diagnosing pneumonia as it would enable him to hear the lungs 'bubbling'. Dr. Brooke, who was not only a fine regional medical officer but also a splendid actor, having graced the boards of the Little Theatre many a time, received this observation with remarkable self-control, asking him simply if he was qualified to use a stethoscope. The technician admitted that he was not qualified to use a stethoscope. Dr. Brooke told him that a bed was not justified and then designated the first aid post as a government grade 'B' dispensary. I was extremely pleased with this new arrangement and the greater control that it brought to the medical services available on the site. The technician was also pleased as he now had the title of dispenser and had direct access to the Arusha hospital where he had to take his register from time to time.

On a few occasions, I detected a faint undercurrent of superstitious fear, of 'wachawi' (i.e. evil spirits) and of 'mumiani' (i.e. use of human blood for magical purposes), among the families living on the T.P.R.I. site. This rarely became apparent, but tended to emerge when campaigns were in progress to obtain blood donors for Arusha hospital or when an unexpected death occurred in the vicinity. One day, I arrived at the office to learn that one of the junior staff had unexpectedly died in the night and had been taken to the mortuary at Arusha hospital. The atmosphere among many of the African staff was extremely oppressive and members of the staff union explained that this was the second recent unexplained

death in the area, although the first one had not been of a staff
member. Thus, there was considerable fear among the families of
some staff residents that some evil force was at hand and that it
could only be dispelled by removal of the staff member's body from
Arusha. Within two hours, the death certificate had been inspected
– it stated that death was due to 'cardiac arrest' – a coffin had been
made up in the T.P.R.I. workshop and the body placed in a T.P.R.I.
landrover and driven out of Arusha. In the company of two
colleagues of the same tribe, the body was taken to the deceased's
home in the Lake Province area of Tanzania to receive an
appropriate burial. When it was known that the landrover had
departed, the oppressive atmosphere instantly lifted and normality
returned.

Endemic plague occurred in the Mbulu mountains about one
hundred miles south-west of Arusha. It rarely spilt over from its
normal wild reservoir of multimammate rats and gerbils, but
nevertheless a few human cases usually occured in that district each
year and were treated locally. However, in 1969, a member of the
Mbulu tribe, admitted into Arusha hospital, was found to have
plague and was suspected of transmitting it pneumonically to one
or two other people in the hospital. The threat of possible
transmission of pneumonic plague throughout Arusha township
was taken most seriously by the East African Community who set
in train the most draconian measures to prevent its reintroduction
and spread within the township. A small plague committee was
established in which I was included and, while I was able to
contribute a little towards improving general sanitation within the
most densely inhabited parts of the town, the emphasis was on
quarantine and mass distribution of 'sulphur-tablets' which
contained a well known antibiotic. A quarantine barrier was set up
on the Babati Road leading from Mbulu to Arusha. Unfortunately,
it was situated just before the road entering into the T.P.R.I.
campus, so that for some days, before the situation could be
rectified, transport between Arusha and T.P.R.I. included cutting
across fields and undeveloped land, even for me to bring the
sulphur tablets to the staff and families resident there. The World
Health Organization had been notified and through its good offices
an aircraft loaded with sulphur tablets arrived at Arusha and

distribution of them began immediately. The daily dose for an adult comprised six or more tablets and several days' tablets for each member of a family were given to the head of each family. Consequently, many heads of families received over one hundred tablets at each distribution. I collected the necessary number of tablets for my wife, servants and myself but our gardener, Jeremiah, while out in the market area of Arusha, joined a somewhat disorganized and vociferous queue, obtained his own tablets and, under a misunderstanding, immediately swallowed a full days dose; he did not feel at all well the next day. No further cases of plague occurred in Arusha so, after two weeks, distribution of sulphur tablets was halted and much publicised requests made for the return of unused tablets. It was just as well that that their distribution stopped then, for many of the public had begun to demand different tablets to treat headaches which they attributed to the sulphur tablets. Afterwards, however, the general reaction of the public was most favourable because many infections, including venereal ones, had been cured or, at least, reduced.

For a period of about a year or so, especially when the Chinese were giving substantial aid towards the establishment of factories and, in particular, the enormous undertaking of building the Tanzania-Zambia railway, it was fashionable to quote the sayings of Mao Tse Tung published in his 'Little Red Book'. A few Chinese were seen in Arusha from time to time, but they kept themselves very much to themselves and their only noticeable influence on the public in general was in the town centre gardens which were planted with ornamental cabbages in place of the usual small flowering shrubs. There was government concern about anglicization of the Swahili language, as in 'breakfasti' and 'weekendi', and I was told that linguists in Dar-es-Salaam were currently introducing new words into the Swahili vocabulary to provide for technical terms and expressions appropriate to modern lifestyles. Under the influence of 'Mwalimu' President Nyerere, there had been a tremendous improvement in literacy among the population. When I first arrived in Tanganyika in 1950, the Tanzanians that I met, seeking work, were never graduates and the few who had a school education were only of the lowest grades. By 1970, my impression was that the national schools and University of

Dar-es-Salaam were turning out more well-educated Africans than the country could provide appropriate work for. Every week, I received scores of letters from well-educated Africans, including graduates, seeking work at T.P.R.I. One or two of the graduates with the right qualifications were taken on for two years training, but most had to be turned away because suitable vacancies only occurred once or twice a year. It seemed that the academic and industrial base of the country was just not large enough to provide appropriate jobs for more than a small proportion of those who graduated each year. It was not uncommon for well-qualified Tanzanians to apply for quite menial posts at the Institute in an attempt to get on the permanent staff and then try to improve their position from there. Another difficulty which started to emerge among the African graduate staff at T.P.R.I. and other departments was the question of career opportunities. Most African incumbents were young, including those in senior posts, and prospects for further promotion, within a reasonable time scale, were perceived as slight as africanization proceeded towards completion.

At the same time as my appointment as Director, Ephata Materu was appointed Deputy Director and shortly afterwards, as Director Designate for a period of two years during which he worked for and obtained an external Ph.D. awarded by Nairobi University. Professor Thomas Odhiambo was internal examiner, and I was external examiner. Ephata Materu took over as Director on 1st April 1970, three years after being appointed Deputy Director. It was a big wrench stepping down from Director, for I had enjoyed every aspect of it, including the prestige of the post, the intellectual stimulation of discussions with research officers and taking an active part in planning a variety of research activities; the administrative contacts with senior officials within headquarters, from other institutes in different parts of East Africa, and from overseas; and the day to day chats, in Swahili, with the many junior African staff. I felt that Ephata should ease himself into the post of Director without me being there to breathe over his shoulder. Accordingly, I went on home leave in late November 1969, returning towards the end of April 1970.

After years of living in Africa, Irene and I thought it might be nice to have a place in the sun to live in at least during part of the year.

157

Hence in 1969, I had a villa built on Tenerife, but with no intentions of keeping it if we did not like it. We arrived on home leave on a cold, foggy day in November and a few days later were aboard one of the Fred Olsen line vessels en route to Tenerife. It was a most enjoyable cruise and absolute bliss entering the sunshine after a couple of days at sea. We became friends with a couple from Worthing, joining in the social activities on board and playing a great deal of table tennis. We disembarked at Santa Cruz de Tenerife and took a taxi up to our villa, which was one of about twenty in a new small development at Las Cuevas, near the lovely old town of La Orotava. On reaching Las Cuevas, we alighted at a *parador* – a lookout bay by the road – very close to the villas. The view was breathtaking. Ahead of us and to the north, the land, covered in banana plantations and clusters of bougainvillea and hibiscus plants, dropped steeply away, presenting an uninterrupted view of some two hundred miles of Atlantic ocean. Behind us, and apparently very close by, was the glittering, snow-capped mountain of El Teide. There were two other people on the parador and one of them asked, 'Are you the Smiths? We have been expecting you.' I commented on the view and asked them if they liked living in Las Cuevas and they replied that it was wonderful. We were introduced to the builder Manuelo and his wife Dolores, who was the landowner. As our villa was unfurnished, we were given temporary accommodation in a furnished villa provided as a rest house for new arrivals. Most of the villas were occupied and we met many of the occupants and had social evenings with them. They were most interesting people from all walks of life; most were also well-travelled and had spent a lot of time abroad in the sun.

After looking over our new villa and admiring its moorish arches, terrazzo floor and *piña riga* – raw pine – woodwork, we were taken in hand by Dolores who whirled us around the steep and spiral roads in her small car, in search of furnishings. We were looking for modern furnishings suitable for a bungalow but Dolores, with the best intentions, took us to retailers in Puerto de La Cruz, most of whom appeared to be relatives, who supplied traditional massive Spanish furniture, Gothic and Plantagenet in appearance. We were also transported rapidly from one retailer to another, each one of whom quickly rolled out many carpets and reels of material. The whole pace was much too fast and Irene developed a headache trying to overcome vertigo on the roads and assimilate the overwhelming numbers of furnishings presented to her. Thus, after a week we had not yet started to furnish the villa. We did not know at that time, but had we been taken to the capital, Santa Cruz de Tenerife, we could have found the furnishings that we were seeking in one day. Within a week, as we got to know our neighbours better, we found that nearly all of them were British, and sensed that some were not quite so enamoured with their choice of retiring on Tenerife as we had previously supposed. We therefore held off buying furniture for another week, during which it became apparent that at least half of them found the status of *El residente* much less attractive that of *El turista*. It was not the fault of the Tenefienos, for they were charming and most helpful people, nor the climate which was perfect. The main factors seemed to be a feeling of isolation, insufficient variety in social activities, and loss of many of the little things that contribute to an essentially British way of life. The Canary Islands were outside the sterling area and some residents could not now afford to return to U.K. as they had only been able to afford a villa in Tenerife by changing domicile, and so avoiding liability to pay the dollar premium of over thirty per cent. In order to sell their villas they would have to first revoke their domicillary status and pay the dollar premium. As I had had to pay the dollar premium when buying the villa this problem did not arise, so, while ackowledging that a fortnight was not long enough to properly evaluate the merits of staying or selling, Irene and I nevertheless concluded that, since we had not yet bought any furniture, a snap decision was required. We came down on the side of selling and placed the property in the reliable hands of estate agent, Mr. Felsing, in Puerto de La Cruz. We decided against renting the villa for we had witnessed several incidences as Las Cuevas where sudden little whirlwinds blew whole areas of tiles off villa roofs. Manuelo quickly restored the roofs but we felt that maintenance of the property at a distance might prove difficult.

Linda and Diana had been looking forward to spending Christmas with us in our new villa on Tenerife and were understandably extremely disappointed when we informed them that we had cancelled their tickets with Iberian Airways and were returning to the U.K. after only a month on the island. We filled in the month quite pleasantly in the company of new acquaintances made at our urbanization. We regularly took coffee in 'The Drum', a restaurant stituated below the floor of a bandstand at La Orotava, and frequently walked down to the thriving holiday resort of Puerto de la Cruz for lunch and a swim in the sea. We returned to London docks on the same ship, the *Black Prince*, and drove down to Bexhill-on-Sea where we rented a house – No. 82, Cooden Drive – until our departure for East Africa at the end of April 1970. We had a white Christmas and the children, who had seen snow on the top of Mount Kilimanjaro, but had never come into contact with it, were absolutely fascinated by snowflakes and the texture of it. We trudged through quite deep snow on the promenade and top of the beach, and built a snowman in the garden. We had an English Christmas with turkey and plum pudding. The next day Linda and I enjoyed making a turkey fricassee but it was quite inedible so it went down the loo. The children made friends locally and Linda spent some time studying for an exam. When the snow had departed, I joined the tennis club in Cooden and, keeping warm in a track suit, enjoyed several games there.

Irene and I returned to Arusha by air and were very happy to be back in our Arusha home and in the East African sunshine. I had been appointed Director (Special Duties) by the East African Community with the assignment of establishing an East African pesticides control organization. During the 1960s, DDT and related insecticides, sprayed indoors on walls and roofs, saved the lives of millions of people in developing countries, by control or eradication of malaria. Similarly, insecticides applied to crops in tropical countries also saved millions of people from starvation. Nevertheless, there was growing opinion expressed, particularly in developed countries, that the large scale use of pesticides was exerting an adverse effect on the environment and, over the long term, even possibly on human health. Many of the earliest comments related to birds and fish. Rachel Carson's book, *Silent Spring*, published in 1962, initiated widespread public interest in the environmental impact of insecticides. She provided numerous examples of high mortalities occurring among natural populations of birds attributable to the effects of insecticides operating through the food chain. Other environmentalists showed that birds and fish, even in remote parts of the world, contained minute quantities of insecticide in their body-fat. These findings had been made possible by remarkable progress in chromatographic techniques used in chemical analysis, whereby concentrations of some insecticides, lower than one part per million, we easily identified. Later studies revealed the presence of minute amounts of insecticides present in the tissue of human beings and even in mother's milk. It was these latter findings which most seemed to upset some of my African colleagues for they regarded it as a violation of human rights and dignity, even though there was no evidence of harmful effects.

In the early 1960s, the World Health Organization and the pesticides chemical industry were already carrying out extensive research to develop bio-degradable insecticides and I was taking a part in trials of them. It was extremely difficult to find cost-effective replacements for non-bio-degradable insecticides such as DDT, and with anything approaching the same level of safety to human beings. The organo-phosphate insecticide, malathion, was the most widely used replacement but even this, because of a combination of higher manufacturing costs and the price of toxicity trials, and its shorter period of effectiveness on mud-lined walls, cost up to eight times more for effective malaria control than DDT. Hence, wherever malaria mosquitoes were still susceptible to DDT, it was still used. The synthetic pyrethroids emerged towards the end of the 1960s; these were not only bio-degradable, but were also extremely safe to human beings. They were, however, even more costly than malathion and few countries could afford substituting them for DDT or malathion for residual spraying of houses. Similarly, in agriculture, DDT was widely employed for control of insect pests on many crops. In Tanzania, for example, where tobacco was an important cash crop, DDT was used to control insect pests in some tobacco plantations. It was against the above background that the East African Pesticides Control Organization was conceived.

I had always harboured concern for the environmental aspects of pesticides usage and had instigated several field studies to evaluate the potential use of more environmentally acceptable insecticides such as naturally occurring pyrethrins and certain synthetic pyrethroids. Also, during my three years as Director of the Tropical

Pesticides Research Organization, I had been actively preparing for the eventual establishment of an East African Pesticides Control Organization. This involved frequent meetings with Mr. Paddock, Chairman of the East African Pesticides Chemical Industry, who not only represented the industry's point of view, but was extremely helpful in advising me on many aspects of this complex assignment. While on home leave in 1968, I spent a few days at Harpenden to visit the headquarters of the United Kingdom Pesticides Approval Organization and received valuable guidance from its Director, Dr. R. de Barry Ashworth. Following my appointment as Director (Special Duties) in 1970, I spent two years drafting an Enabling Bill to provide the necessary legislation for the proposed E.A. Pesticides Control Organization to be formed and operate. I also developed detailed proposals for offices, laboratories, establishment, duties of the staff, and related financial estimates. Temporary offices were formed in Arusha township through conversion of premises that had previously been used as a dress shop, the 'Vogue'. In due course, the Enabling Bill was drafted but, to become effective, it required signatures of the Authority (i.e. the Presidents of Kenya, Tanzania and Uganda). Regrettably, General Amin was then President of Uganda and too involved in civil war to take time off to sign the document. Consequently, the E.A. Pesticides Control Organization was never formed and even the East African Community as a whole felt the strain of his presence and did not survive beyond 1977. However, my work was not entirely in vain for it was found useful by the World Health Organization in establishing its own programme relating to the safe use of pesticides, and as one of the East African Community delegation attending the first United Nations conference on the human environment, held in Stockholm in June 1972, I was able to vote in favour of a new United Nations Agency, the U.N. Environment Protection Agency (U.N.E.P.) to be established in Nairobi.

I left East Africa on compulsory retirement leave in November 1972, as required under the East African Community Africanization Programme, but with no hard feelings, for I had been fortunate to have been allowed to remain working in Tanzania for eleven years after its independence. Although many of our friends and colleagues had departed before then, there were still many left, and Irene and I were wined and dined for weeks before our departure by our African, Asian and European friends. A touching farewell party and parting gift of an engraved silver tankard was given by the staff of the Tropical Pesticides Research Institute, followed by the customary group photograph published in local papers and the East African Community magazine. There was a farewell evening at the Arusha Gymkhana Club and the tennis section gave Irene and me a copper salver. After Irene and I had given our last performance with the Arusha Amateur Theatrical Society, only a month before our departure, we received a nice address from the stage and warm applause from the audience. It was an emotional time. Our servants cried and we were sorry to leave our lovely home and familiar surroundings of East Africa. We sold a few, and gave away many, of our household effects, and I gave away many of my technical books to African staff members of the Tropical Pesticides Research Institute, for there was a desperate need for them. During this time, I did, however, have the cold sense to make photocopies of my salary record sheets from 1st July 1962 onwards, without which the delay in authorising my Crown Agent's pension may have extended even beyond August 1973, when the commuted portion was eventually paid, and beyond October 1973, when annual payments commenced. We boxed up our remaining household effects and, after customs clearance in Arusha, had them shipped to the U.K. and placed in storage. With the essential exit permits stamped in our passports, following payment of designated outstanding income tax, we returned to the U.K. by air and drove to Bexhill where we again rented No. 82, Cooden Drive through Mrs Helen Cummings, as we had done during our previous home leave.

Although I had six months' retirement leave, had already received a generous golden handshake, and within a few months could expect a decent pension, I found it extremely difficult to be professionally inactive; and so, when offered employment with the World Health Organization in March 1973, I readily accepted it. The first eight months of this post were spent in Geneva headquarters assisting in evaluation of results of field trials in Kenya and Nigeria, including a short visit to each of these

163

countries. Irene stayed in Bexhill for a few months to oversee the purchase of a garden flat, for we felt that it was now essential to have a *pied à terre* in England, and then joined me in a hotel in Geneva.

5

Southern Africa

Working for WHO, and living in Switzerland, was very different from being employed in Her Majesty's Colonial Service, or by the Ministry of Overseas Development, and living in Tanzania. The salary was considerably higher but so was the official cost of living. I never quite adjusted to the noise of city life and the more sophisticated urban life-style of Geneva compared with that of Arusha. Most noticeable differences were the extremely efficient public and banking services in Geneva. After receiving unhurried service over many years, often involving extensive greetings, errors and corrections, I was frequently disconcerted by the speed with which I was served and, at first, would often wait for further attention when none was due. The WHO main building, although only a fraction of the size of the nearby ILO building, was most impressive with its marble-floored and pillared entrance hall and its impeccably groomed staff. I bought a couple of good suits to conform with appearances but felt uneasy in them, particularly in the warm weather which I associated with shorts and a light shirt.

I already had a high regard for the aims of the World Health Organization to protect and promote human health – defined in the WHO Constitution of 7th April 1948 as 'A state of complete physical, mental and social well-being and not merely the absence of disease or infirmity'. I also believed, as stated in the Constitution, that 'the enjoyment of the highest attainable standard of health is one of the fundamental rights of every human being without distinction of race, religion, political belief, economic or social condition'. It was only after some months of working with the Organization that I became aware of its many and varied activities, and its outstanding achievements, accomplished with a total staff of only about 4,500 and a regular budget quite small in global terms, being perhaps equal to that of a medium-sized university in the United States. Fortunately, additional funding is obtained through voluntary contributions by countries or other international organizations. As an entomologist, I was interested in WHO's worldwide epidemiological service whereby it received and disseminated information from countries on instances of outbreaks of quarantinable diseases including plague, yellow fever, typhus and relapsing fever, and other important vector – borne diseases such as malaria, dengue haemorrhagic fever and Japanese encephalitis. I was also interested in WHO's development of international health regulations.

An outstanding advisory service, provided by WHO, is bringing together experts from different countries to conferences or expert committees to analyse specific health problems and make recommendations on how they should be tackled. I participated in several expert committees and their findings were published in WHO technical reports. Another advisory service aimed at strengthening countries' health services is in the form of projects of generally two to five years' duration. These are requested by a national government which is in administrative control, with WHO's participation being complimentary. The government shares the cost with WHO, provides counterpart staff who will eventually take over the work, and makes practical arrangements for carrying out the work when WHO assistance comes to an end.

In November 1973, I was assigned to a malaria control project, relating to Southern Africa, and based in South Africa. Irene and I flew by Swiss Air. The day of departure was extremely cold and take off delayed by snow on the runway. After waiting on board for several hours, we were transferred at 2 a.m. to an hotel in Geneva until daybreak when we were able to board the aircraft again. The flight was a good twelve hours' duration and included a stopover at Nairobi airport for refuelling. We arrived at Jan Smuts international airport in Johannesburg to be greeted by Dr Frank Hansford, Director of the Siegfried Annecke Malaria Research

Institute which was situated in Tzaneen, a small town in the Northern Transvaal. It was nice to get back into the sun and warmth of Africa but, after sitting in the aircraft for many hours, Irene and I were too fatigued and cramped to get the best out of the four hundred miles car journey to Tzaneen. Once outside Joahnnesburg and its high-rise buildings, we passed the mining area of the rand with its ochrous hill-sized mounds of waste. Some were being grassed over but others were being surface-mined for their small quantities of residual gold. It seemed that the price of gold had risen so much, and techniques of extraction had so improved since the mounds were made many years ago, that re-processing the waste was now well worth-while. The remainder of the route passed largely through agricultural land with its extensive crops of wheat and maize and, nearer Tzaneen, plantations of sugar cane and citrous crops. Herds of cattle, goats and sheep were less frequently seen. I was, however, particularly struck by the goats, all of which had much shorter legs than I had been accustomed to seeing in other parts of Africa.

We stopped for lunch at a cafe in Nylstroom where I had my first South African T-bone steak. It was delicious and huge – a typical 'plate-hanger', as they were sometimes called. Irene was recovering from a cold and was not her usual buoyant self. Nevertheless, she revived at one point during the journey to enquire if there was any housing for us. This has almost invariably proved to be a 'good question' when asked by new arrivals, and indeed she received the not unexpected answer that housing accommodation was not quite ready as progress in building it had been slower than anticipated, and that arrangements had been made to accommodate us provisionally in the Tzaneen Hotel. We passed through Pietersburgh and met officials in the Ministry of Health building there, and then continued on to Tzaneen, arriving at the hotel in the evening.

Before 1946, seasonal malaria was rife in the Transvaal and prevented agricultural development in much of this fertile area. The history of misery and sorrow caused by malaria to the early settlers is to this day reflected in the names of many towns and places in the Transvaal. There were serious epidemics in 1939 and 1943 in both of which thousands of people, of all races, died. Shortly after the

end of the second world war, Dr Siegfried Annecke commenced a
war on malaria by spraying huts and houses with DDT, and by
1949, blackwater fever, the scourge of the low veld had vanished
and the incidence of malaria in the Transvaal reduced to an
extremely low level. This situation persisted until 1972, permitting
tremendous developments in agriculture and mining to take place.
However, in 1972 there was a flare-up of malaria with 3,731 cases
detected. The reason for the outbreak was not known because local
expertise in malaria research had not been needed for over twenty
years and was no longer available. The South African government
brought this situation to the attention of WHO who considered
that it required investigation as it had wider implications for other
areas of Southern Africa. Consequently, a small project was drawn
up and a research team formed, comprising three WHO staff,
epidemiologist (Nederlander), demographer (American) and entomologist (British), with counterpart national staff provided by the
Siegfried Annecke Institute.

After preliminary surveys, we selected an area in the Sibasa
District for the project. The project area lay in the extreme north of
the Transvaal within a short distance of the mighty Limpopo river
which separated South Africa from Zimbabwe. A field laboratory
and basic accommodation were established in a government rest
house in Makonde village which was fairly centrally situated in the
project area. The inhabitants were of the Venda tribe and they lived
in thatched rondavels not uncommonly furnished to a surprisingly
high standard. Many had chests of drawers and beds with
mattresses, and some even had wardrobes. In other respects their
way of life and dress were traditional. Their chief lived on the side
of a hill and his compound was approached by a winding track
bounded by stretches of dry stone walling resembling that of the
ancient stone city of Mapungubwe in the Northern Transvaal. Even
more interesting was that some sections of the stone walling had a
lattice pattern resembling those in the stone walls of the even older
stone city of Great Zimbabwe in Zimbabwe (Southern Rhodesia).
Quite a high proportion of Venda maintained ancient tribal beliefs,
including wearing old beads which represented their ancestors.
Some of the girls also took part in elaborate domba ceremonies
relating to preparation for marriage. I saw one domba dance in

which girls formed a sinuous line resembling a snake, and also a huge domba drum suspended inside a shelter. Outside the project area, Venda-land extended into the Soutpansberg mountains in which lies the fearsome Lake Fundudzi. On approach to the lake, tradition required that obeisance be made by turning the back, bending over double, and viewing it respectfully from between the legs. As with Lake Chala in Kenya, there was also a belief that a village lay drowned below the surface. Unlike East Africa, there was no overt fear of 'mumiani' and my work was in no way impeded by tribal beliefs and superstitions. There was a sociological impediment but this was a more recent one. This was that, except for the very old and very young, nearly all the menfolk were away most of the year working in the mines on the Rand. In preparation for their return for the Christmas holidays, the Venda wives would re-decorate their rondavels, including re-plastering them indoors. This more recent custom had to be taken into account in malaria control as it affected the timing of insecticide applications indoors.

The South African government issued me with a white Volkswagen mini-bus or 'kombi' fitted with mud-grip tyres. I first thought that this type of vehicle would prove to be a poor alternative to the landrover whose wonderful performance in the field I had been grateful for many times in the past. To my surprise, however, it turned out to be the ideal vehicle. While not so good as the landrover in highly eroded terrain with steep gullies, it took difficult road surfaces in its stride, including deep sand and mud. It could also seat eight passengers quite comfortably and was far more economical on petrol than a landrover. In East Africa I was accustomed to going on safari for a period sometimes of several months and then returning home. In the Transvaal it was customary for many government staff, working in the field, to have a weekly routine of driving into the field each Monday morning, living and working there under quite simple conditions, and returning home each Friday evening. I adopted the Transvaal way, making use of a Government rest house in the village of Makonde which was fairly centrally situated in the project area. I used part of the rest house as an entomological laboratory and put up my camp bed in another room. I took sufficient cold food to last a week, a thermos of hot coffee, and two jerry cans of cold water for drinking and washing.

It took several months to recruit and train African staff, mostly of the Venda tribe, for the mosquito work, which involved collecting mosquitoes in different ways, breeding adult mosquitoes out from collected larvae, and making very simple groupings of collected material for my further inspection and dissection where appropriate. An initial difficulty, which disappeared as we worked together, was that the African staff seemed to feel a certain unease about working in a laboratory as this was deemed 'White man's work'. The main difficulty, however, was that, after nearly thirty years of house-spraying with residual insecticides, the anopheline mosquito fauna had almost completely changed and was largely unidentifiable at species level. There were strange sibling species, seasonally different polymorphic forms, and one abundant species that seemed to be a new record for South Africa and indistinguishable from *Anopheles flavicosta*, a species commonly found in Madagascar. Few mosquitoes went indoors, so there was a lot of searching for them resting outdoors and collecting of mosquitoes biting throughout the night. The work was physically demanding and I quickly lost all the weight gained during the months spent in Geneva. Hours of walking were, however, immensely eased by a pair of incredibly comfortable field boots given me by the South African government. The sun was surprisingly fierce during the hot months around December when some of the white men that regularly worked in the veld developed tans extending to a deep shade of purple. The nights could also be very cold between June and August, so that mosquito collections made in the hour before dawn were often done at temperatures close to freezing point.

The expression 'Thank God it's Friday' took on a whole new meaning as I drove the hundred and twenty or so miles back to Tzaneen, trying hard not to be caught out by speed traps across the road. I do not think that my Corps Consular registered number plates saved me, but the underpowered engine probably did, as the kombi only went too fast on downhill slopes. I regularly broke the return journey by stopping at a roadside cafe in Louis Trichart and there, surrounded by burly Afrikaaners, would sit over a pot of coffee and smoke the first cigar of the week feeling nothing but bliss, like the character in the advertisement for 'Hamlet' cigars. Apart from when among my own colleagues, this was one of the few occasions in South Africa when I sat among white men in numbers. I met few in the field and, of these, nearly all were middle-aged and included several former British colonials who had come down south after the East and Central African countries had become independent. I was told that city life had more appeal to many young South Africans these days with the exception of those working on their own family farms or in the forces.

A few weeks after our arrival, Linda and Diana came out for their Christmas holidays. They had met old East African boy-friends at Heathrow Airport and had a good chat about old times and current holiday arrangements. Irene had not quite recovered from her cold, so I drove down in the kombi and brought them up from Jan Smuts International Airport. As I was waiting in the arrivals hall, I happened to notice an extremely attractive woman some distance away. To my surprise, she waved and called, 'Alec, it's Molly'. Indeed, it was Molly Long who, with her husband Mike, had been next-door neighbours to Irene and me in Arusha. She was also waiting for her children. I told her that I was based in Tzaneen and she informed me that she and Mike were in Mbabane, Swaziland, where Mike was in agricultural research.

Irene and I were still staying at the Tzaneen Hotel, but while I had been working up country, Irene had been round the estate agents in Tzaneen and, after much diligence, had located a bungalow – No. 34, Harry Dilly Street – available for a long rental. It stood on a small, but attractive plot of land and was within easy walking distance of the hotel and principal shops. We took over the tenancy just before Christmas, and on Christmas Day spent a few hours sitting inside the unfurnished building discussing how we were going to furnish it, how much it would cost and how much money we would need to have sent out. We all had a very pleasant evening, with Christmas dinner at the Hansfords' attractive home among the orange plantations. Linda and Diana enjoyed their holiday based at the Tzaneen hotel; they made full use of its swimming pool and the gorgeous weather, and made several friends through the daughter of the proprietor of the hotel. They seemed to get on equally well with young Afrikaners as with their primarily English-speaking counterparts. I was glad that they did not get involved or see any 'khaki bashing'. This was an infrequent occurrence in Tzaneen but it apparently usually took place in the late evening after heavy drinking and ended up with fights between young Afrikaners and English speakers. The expression dates back to the Boer War when the Afrikaner soldiers had no uniforms but the British ranks were dressed in khaki.

After Linda and Diana had returned to school, Irene and I set about furnishing the bungalow. We assumed that we would not want the hard furnishings after completion of the assignment and that we would then practically have to give them away. We bought a serviceable, but quite revolting, second-hand bedroom suite of 1920s design made in wood of a yellowish hue that clashed garishly with the faded duck-egg blue wall of the master bedroom. With a new mattress, the bed and the room were paradise after a week in the field. More care was taken over furnishing the living room whose french windows opened onto a small patio. We bought quite a nice second-hand three-piece-suite and a good dining table with matching wheel-backed chairs. Our personal effects from East Africa had never been unpacked and when these arrived, some months later, the living room was transformed, especially after the addition of a nice mahogany glass cabinet to house some good pieces. The other two rather small bedrooms were simply furnished with second-hand pieces, but the kitchen was quite decently equipped, including a new electric cooker. There was a fitted calor-gas fire in the lounge.

Soon after moving in, we sent out word that we were looking for a maid. There was no shortage of applicants and within a day or two we had selected a cheerful, chubby, young African woman, Jane, who had previously worked for an Afrikaner family, had quite a good reference, and spoke sufficient English for us to understand her without much difficulty. Within a few yards of the bungalow was a small, brick-built, unfurnished building available for use as resident servants' quarters. Some townspeople preferred to have their servants come to work every day, from outside the town. Resident servants were, however, permitted, provided they were registered with the civic authorities. We offered her quarters and bought her a small cupboard and a new sprung bed, complete with mattress. She was overcome with the bed, having expected a camp bed or 'stretcher-bed' as she called it. We also took on a garden boy, Patrick, and acquired two siamese cats, 'Twinky' and 'Twonky'. Twinky, a female, was given by one of my WHO colleagues, and Twonky, a male, by a neighbour after it had spent the greater part of three months on our premises, apparently having difficulty in staying away from Twinky. They would spend hours snuggled up together on one of the more comfortable chairs.

Jane set about cleaning the house like a human dynamo, until everything shone. It was apparent that her previous employer had been quite a firm one and kept her house almost surgically clean. She turned out to be a competent cook and, on request, would occasionally prepare an Afrikaner meal such as boerwurst and mealie-pop with traditional tomato relish. It was delicious, as were the garlic sausages bought at an Afrikaner butchers some miles out of town. Jane was very happy with her quarters and before long her mother moved in with her and, on Sunday afternoons, Jane sometimes held well-conducted garden parties on our back lawn for her friends. In addition to their wages, African staff were required, by law, to be adequately fed daily by their employer. Jane loved her food. Each day she ate more meat than both Irene and I, and cooked an enormous saucepan of mealie-pop, theoretically enough for ten people. One Christmas, she asked Irene if she could make a 'few' scones. Irene found herself providing rather more ingredients than expected, for Jane made several very large bags of scones which Patrick took down to the market for sale to raise funds to meet Jane's own Christmas expenses. Irene and I found this incident quite amusing but told Jane once was enough.

One of Patrick's main duties developed into helping Irene with the shopping. While the repugnant system of apartheid operated in hotels and government institutions such as the post office, banks and railways, it did not occur in large multiple stores such as the O.K. Bazaar where blacks and whites freely mingled in purchasing and pushing their shopping trolleys around. There were even shops such as grocers and off-licences run by whites and aimed at the 'Bantu' trade. While I soon noticed that most of the Africans that I had seen in the field and in Tzaneen Township looked in better

physical health than those in some of the most rural parts of East
Africa, it took me longer to become aware that the so-called 'Bantu'
trade formed an important part of the Transvaal economy for,
although their individual wages were low, their combined spending
power was considerable.

Soon after furnishing the house, I bought a second hand Ford
Corsair car for running around Tzaneen at weekends. In doing so, I
learnt the Afrikaans word 'voetstoet', used in the sense of 'old
banger', and translating into 'kick-start', an expression I had never
heard before but which is frequently used nowadays by economists.
I already had Tanzania and U.K. driving licences, the latter gained
in Hastings one day during retirement leave in 1973, but neither
licence met the South African requirement of having a photograph
of the driver as well as signature and date. On the day the test was
due, the 'voetstoet' refused to start and I had to take the test in the
recently issued mini-bus whose small rear window provided limited
visibility and was less than ideal for the purpose. The test was
facilitated by driving in South Africa being on the left-hand side of
the road as in the U.K., but how I managed to reverse cleanly
between four sisal poles, I shall never know; thank heavens the test
required it to be done only once.

Irene and I developed quite a pleasant social life during the
weekends. On Friday evenings Jane, whose young eyes had the
vision of a hawk, would first spot the approaching kombi and clap
her hands shouting, 'Madam, the master's coming'. The cats would
recognize the sound of the engine and come skidding into the
driveway. Patrick would rush to take the safari gear out of the
vehicle and receive my dusty or muddy boots for polishing to a high
sheen ready for the following Monday morning. I would give Irene
a hug and, after a good hot bath and change of clothes, settle down
to a comfortable evening and the first cold beer and hot dinner of
the week. We had bought an almost new piano from the wife of an
Afrikaner on a farm, whose young daughter had lost interest in it.
Sometimes Irene would play the piano, or we would go to the local
cinema, or 'bioscope' as it was sometimes called, but most evenings
we played bridge with our English-speaking neighbours, Neil and
Sheila Trollope. I played tennis a few times at the local club. The
members were most welcoming but conversation and scoring were

normally in Afrikaans, and my knowledge of the language was almost nil. The effort with the language was more than I wanted at the weekend, so I took up golf. I joined the Magoebaskloof golf club, and Neil and I played regularly there and also at the nearby Orangedean golf club, with which there was reciprocal membership. Magoebaskloof golf club was wonderfully situated on the lower slopes of the mighty Drakensberg mountains. When the air was clear, the views anywhere on the golf course were spectacular. The course was hilly and there were some challengingly placed greens, a delight to play but requiring at least double bogies from my game. Neil was a much longer hitter, however, and made par on some of them seem easy. Orangedean club also had its attractions because it was surrounded by plantations of orange trees whose scented blossom filled the air in season. Irene and I would often have a weekend lunch in the Tzaneen hotel, after which I would enjoy its swimming pool. The water was quite cold between June and August when I frequently had the pool to myself.

Occasionally, Irene and I would drive out for the day to visit some of the beautifully scenic and historically interesting places close by. We lived in the lowlands (low veld), but just a few miles east of the Drakensberg mountains. These formed a chain, about a thousand miles long, stretching from north to south and dividing the lowlands from the highlands by an escarpment (part of the Great Rift wall) over one thousand five hundred feet high. Remnants of the old precipitous nineteenth century coach road were visible, but this had long been superseded by a winding and modern tarmac road which provided a very pleasant run from the heat of Tzaneen to the cooler air of Magoebaskloof and Stanford Lake, where we occasionally had lunch at a nice hotel overlooking the Ebenezer Dam. In the spring (September to November) we drove on to Haenertsburg to see magnificent displays of cherry blossom and azalea. Sometimes we visited the nearby Debegeni Falls for a picnic among the trees and, along with other, generally more youthful, visitors, I would enjoy the exciting natural water-slide formed in the rock of the river bed. Another pleasant drive was to the small picturesque town of Duiwelskloof, about twenty miles north of Tzaneen. Neil and Sheila showed us some attractive and interesting places to the south of Tzaneen including some impressive waterfalls, a spectacular view (resembling a miniature Grand Canyon) from 'God's Window', and the perfectly preserved old gold-mining village of Pilgrim's Rest. There were several old pit-mines, with their entrances now blocked up but with sections of old railway lines still in evidence. I was particularly impressed by the relatively large graveyard with epitaphs on the tombstones indicating the decimating effects of malaria in the Transvaal during the nineteenth century.

One of the difficulties in controlling malaria in Southern Africa was the movement of Africans from highly malarious areas to areas where malaria was under a high level of control. Each month, many Africans crossed the border from Mozambique into South Africa with the intention of living and working illegally in South Africa. Most of them were infected with malaria and presented a reservoir of parasites to vector mosquitoes breeding in the Transvaal. Early in the assignment, our project team went across to Komatipoort, on the border of the two countries, to discuss the epidemiological aspects of this problem with the Mozambique Health Authorities and consider possible ways of improving malaria control each side of the border. On the way we stopped at Mbabane, the capital of Swaziland, to introduce ourselves to the Health Authorities and brief them on our assignment.

About a year later, I followed up this visit by spending a week in Mbabane to collect mosquitoes for comparative purposes. Irene came with me and we stayed with Molly and Mike Long for a few days at their home in Mbabane. Mike took us to the club, where we were greeted by shouts of 'Hujambo' from several old friends and acquaintances whom we had known in Arusha. There was a good meeting at the club that day because an official from the Ministry of Overseas Development was there to talk about upwardly-revised conditions of service, including education and passage allowances. It was all very nostalgic. One offspin of working in Africa, over many years, was that one often met old colleagues, friends and acquaintances, sometimes in unexpected circumstances. A good example occurred on the way to Mbabane. Irene and I had been driving for some hours and were well out in the open countryside of the low veld when we came to a small 'dorp', or village. The surrounding scene was like a desert with dusty, flat terrain stretching as far as the eye could see, broken only by a few buildings at a crossroads. The wind was howling and balls of cactus were blowing across the landscape. One of the buildings was a general store and, on impulse, I stopped to buy some razor blades. Hardly had I got through the door when a voice said, 'Alec Smith, what on earth are you doing here?'. It was Kirsten Jorgensen, one of the prettiest young ladies to have graced the boards and Arusha Ghymkhana Club tennis courts during my years in Arusha. She introduced Irene and me to her husband who was sitting in a car nearby; he was farming somewhere in the area.

Apartheid was at least as strict in the church as in many other institutions. Irene and I did not feel at all at ease attending a whites only church but, as we both felt the need to worship, we usually went to Sunday morning service at the nearby Methodist church. The church was well-attended and the congregation impeccably attired, with many of the ladies wearing wide-brimmed hats and white, elbow-length gloves. The minister gave wonderful sermons that held the attention from beginning to end. There was an air of deep devotion and a few members were even known to have spoken in tongues. Irene taught in the Sunday School and gave free tuition in English and History to several children who attended the church. She also taught the Church of England Sunday School children on Thursday afternoons, and produced the exceedingly well-attended nativity play for Christmas 1974, when Diana played the recorder as part of the programme. The churches for Africans were also well-attended, and each Sunday a procession of immaculately dressed worshippers passed by our house, many of the men in suits and the ladies in bright clothes and bonnets, having laid aside their usual black berets for a day.

By the summer of 1974, Linda had completed her 'A' levels and Diana her 'O' levels. At that time, it was quite usual for students to take a year off before going on to university. Linda proposed to stay with us in South Africa for a year before going up to Sussex, and Diana, who had found eight years in boarding school quite enough, wanted to come out with Linda. Taking into account that both our daughters had been deprived of a lot of home life in recent years, Irene and I considered that, on balance, it would be better if they both came out together. We drove down in the kombi and met them at Jan Smuts International Airport. They had not felt hungry during the flight but rapidly demolished two enormous meals each in a 'Golden Egg' road-side restaurant a little way out of Johannesburg.

Linda worked for several months in a stationer's office in Tzaneen, and Diana in the Tzaneen public library before going to a secretarial college in Johannesburg for a few months. The remaining months were spent largely around the swimming pool of the Tzaneen Hotel with their friends including Marie MacAskill, the daughter of the proprietor of the hotel. They made friends with Rob and Edgar, two British geologists whom they usually invited round to our bungalow each Sunday evening for dinner and a game of bridge. An amusing aspect of these evenings was that, on successive Sundays, Irene and the two friends took turns in cooking the dinner. Rob had a girl friend, Myra, in the UK and, shortly after she came out for a holiday, they got married in the Catholic church in Tzaneen. I gave Myra away and Linda and Diana dressed up to the hilt. Linda, still in wide-brimmed hat and floating dress, fell into a swimming pool during the wedding festivities, after which her dress was always referred to as the swimming pool dress.

Through the church, Diana met Lindsey Robertson through whom both our families became great friends. We would frequently visit his parents, Ian and Rhoda, at home at nearby 'Hobsons Choice', a farm under Ian's management. Ian and Rhoda were both South Africans, born and bred, but Ian had a strong attachment to his Scottish roots and, on the least excuse, would stride up and down the stoep playing his bagpipes. We enjoyed tea around their swimming pool from where there was a wonderful view across their orange plantation of the sharply toothed Drakensberg mountain range. Linda also had a friend, Peter, in the UK, and would frequently write inviting him out. One day, to her surprise, he replied that he was giving up his studies and coming out. He was an extremely talented young painter and was our guest for several weeks before moving on to stay with Rhoda and Ian. Linda and Diana made great friends with Jane and would talk to her for hours. Jane distinguished between two types of boy friend, 'rich' and 'white trash', the latter category being children of the less well-off. When Linda and Diana were going out in the evening,

Jane would invariably shout after them, 'Remember, keep away from them white trash!'

Although 1974 was the year of the oil crisis in which the price of oil rose from two or three dollars to nearly forty dollars a barrel, there was no petrol rationing in South Africa, in spite of the country having no natural deposits of oil. It seemed that there were good reserves and that petrol was being refined from coal. The overseas newspapers were full of the financial crisis but in South Africa the problem was often played down or even treated with amusement, one popular remark being that the time to buy War Loan was when the annual interest was the same as its price i.e. £19, which did occur briefly.

We went on home leave in August 1975 by direct flight from Jan Smuts to Heathrow, for, by then, aircraft had been adapted to carry enough fuel to avoid a stopover. Regulations allowed us six weeks leave a year with home leave passages paid every two years. The leave was largely based on our Bexhill flat and the nearby beach, and time flew by. Friends were, not unnaturally, far more interested in home matters such as house prices than in events down south. Indeed, as long as apartheid prevailed, very few wanted to hear a word about South Africa. In September we went up to Sussex University to help Linda settle into residence; and then to Oxford to assist Diana settle into that renowned secretarial college widely known as the 'Ox and Cow'. I spent an additional week on study-leave, working at the British Museum on the taxonomy of mosquitoes collected from the project area.

On returning to Tzaneen, I continued working, as before, in the project area, but with more emphasis on training African staff. The weekends also continued to be a complete and welcome contrast. We continued our friendship with Rob and Edgar and Rhoda and Ian, as well as with Neil and Sheila. Irene also made friends with more ladies in the church and this led to her being invited to occasional games of bridge in the afternoons. Towards the end of September 1976, I became involved in handing over the project to Frank Hansford as Director of the Siegfried Annecke Institute, and writing up my assignment report for WHO headquarters. It had been physically demanding field work but of great technical interest, and a good mosquito surveillance system had been built up to complement the parasitological one. I had also taught several Africans basic mosquito taxonomy and, it was jokingly pointed out to me that in doing so I had, in principle, created an administrative problem, for they were not expected to know more than their white senior officers. In practice, this was not so, for times were changing and there was increasing racial tolerance, particularly in the academic institutions.

Although it is rather a trite phrase, it is nice to be appreciated, and the staff of the Siegfried Annecke Institute were very generous in their thanks for the work that I had done. They gave Irene and me a lively farewell party attended by the South African Minister of Health. He told me that the internationally renowned entomologist, Botha de Meillon, would soon be leaving South Africa to live in retirement in America, and that I could be his natural successor in South Africa. I explained that, while I found the entomological work in South Africa extremely interesting, I proposed to stay in the World Health Organization until my own retirement. Before we departed, as in the past, Irene and I had to practically give away many of our hard furnishings. We gave Jane and her mother two new mattresses and bed linen, and afterwards, they invited us to their home and gave us tea and cakes. Their house was one of many identical ones in an unattractive large suburban situation reserved entirely for Africans and built within a street plan of the grid type. The house was a small, detached, brick-built and gable-ended bungalow, and the streets were clean and had overhead electric lights. It was simply furnished but quite homely, and we were made very welcome, even by their neighbours. Irene found Jane work with a lady from the church and Patrick was employed by a neighbour. Twinky, to our great dismay, disappeared one night. It was suggested that she might have been stolen for sale outside Tzaneen. Twonky, however, stayed with us and Rhoda took him over just before we left.

On learning that my next assignment was to be in Nigeria, we sent about half of our personal effects to the UK and placed the rest in storage in South Africa until we had an address in Nigeria. We flew directly from Jan Smuts to Geneva for a few days briefing and then on to Nigeria, arriving at Lagos International Airport on 23rd November 1976.

6

West Africa

As we stepped out of the air-conditioned aircraft, we were hit by intense heat reflecting off the tarmac, an air temperature in the order of 85 degrees Fahrenheit and an extremely high atmospheric humidity. During the previous two weeks, we had changed from living in the hot Transvaal to Geneva with its prevailing 'bise', a penetrating, icy wind that seems to cut through you unless you are wearing a really warm coat. Hence I disembarked wearing a heavy sheepskin coat, for both hands were required to carry the hand luggage. A new international airport had been built since I had visited Nigeria on a WHO consultancy in 1963, but the human scene was essentially the same. The arrivals hall was packed and abuzz with Nigerians dressed in their colourful national costumes. There was little sign of order and the long queues moved agonisingly slowly in the hot and suffocating atmosphere. The manner of the passport control officials was slightly intimidating, conveying a sense of power and one's fate being in their hands, but, on seeing the light blue cover of the WHO 'laissez-passer' and Irene's 'Carte de legitimation', their attitude became much more pleasant. It took over three hours to emerge from the airport and I can well believe a story told of a couple who, years previously, found it all too much on arrival, and returned on the next flight back.

We were met by John Storey, a WHO colleague, and taken to the Mission Rest House in the city centre, where we were made most welcome and stayed a week so that I could work on the project plan with my colleague, in consultation with the WHO representative.

During the intervening weekend, Irene and I went to the Ikoyi Gymkhana Club for lunch. Here, good order reigned with echoes of the colonial past. After an excellent meal served impeccably in an air-conditioned restaurant, we enjoyed walking around the grounds observing that nearly all members were Nigerians and that the squash courts and the nearby golf course were as fully booked as ever. We took a short walk outside the club to admire the beautifully kept, old, colonial houses in their lovely gardens. These houses were large two-storey buildings with reception rooms on the ground floor and bedrooms above them, which usually had quite large balconies. The houses were built long before air conditioners were available, the upper rooms being better ventilated and much cooler than the lower ones, and also less plagued by mosquitoes. Many were apparently now occupied by diplomats or senior expatriate businessmen at rentals well in excess of £20,000 per annum. Old colonial houses, anywhere in Africa, seemed to be much sought after by their successors; even the old German houses in Tanganyika were much admired by the British. We hailed a taxi through the club doorman. Hardly had it moved off when another taxi appeared behind it. There then followed a quite frightening car chase with our taxi being repeatedly hit from behind, and the other taxi sometimes drawing alongside with the driver shouting 'You fit die' at our driver who responded with 'You no kill um'. After about twenty minutes, the chase was discontinued. It was not known what had triggered the incident off, but there had been loss of face by the pursuing taxi driver, and that was almost everything to many Nigerians.

While malaria transmission had been drastically reduced in a few parts of Africa south of the Sahara, such as the Transvaal and the Kenya Highlands, high levels of malaria transmission were still maintained in most of West, Central and East Africa. Field trials carried out in the Garki District of Kano State in Nigeria between 1970 and 1975 showed that malaria control could not be easily achieved in the Sudan savannah ecotype prevalent in that area. It was, however, possible that malaria control could be achieved in other ecological strata widespread throughout West Africa. The present project was therefore designed to conduct applied field research on the epidemiology and control of malaria in different

182

ecological strata. The Bendel State in Nigeria offered access, within relatively short distances, to four different types of ecological strata, and was therefore selected by Nigeria and WHO for the Project.

After a week in Lagos, we were driven to Benin City, the capital of Bendel State. Although the journey was only one hundred and eighty miles, we passed through several towns, some quite large, and, as in Lagos, overcrowded with people and traffic, and hives of human activity. The Nigerians, from 'big-big' men to petty traders with their small roadside stalls, made a lively scene in their colourful robes of national costume, and almost ceaseless business discussions characterised by heated conversation punctuated with bursts of uninhibited laughter. There was also a great movement of people, walking along the edge of the roads, to their work some miles away, and along the roadsides were vendors with their charcoal braziers offering hot corn cobs to passers-by. Many of the town houses were quite large double-storied buildings, brick-built, externally rendered with ochrous-coloured plaster, and roofed with extremely rusty corrugated iron sheeting. The roads were jammed with cars, many of which looked as if they had been roughly restored after severe accidents. There were numerous garishly re-painted buses, some carrying quotations such as 'There is only one God' or 'Inshallah', and nearly all grossly overcrowded. There was a national driving code, but in practice this seemed to have been widely replaced by three simple guidelines to be used when in a traffic jam or approaching an accident: to sound the 'hooter' on the slightest pretext; to lean out of the car window and shout 'I beg you', preferably simultaneously lowering the head so that it came below that of the other driver; and finally to rely entirely on the Will of God. It was not surprising, therefore, to see the main roads littered with the wrecks of vehicles that had been in road accidents. What I had not expected, though, was to see the extent to which so many vehicles had been concertinaed by huge juggernauts that ran between Lagos in the south, and Kano and beyond in the north. Dead bodies were also occasionally seen on the road because other motorists, who were in no way responsible for these deaths, but who stopped to remove the dead, were sometimes hacked to death by people living in the locality.

On arrival at Benin City, we only had to be accommodated in a hotel for three weeks before we were able to move into a house. The Emotan hotel was a modern, high-rise building set in attractive gardens with coloured umbrellas under the trees. It was managed by Nigerians who were pleasant, attentive and conveyed an air of efficiency even when the situation sometimes fell well short of it. Our room was generally well serviced and the air conditioner, that 'blessing from God' as one Nigerian colleague called it, was working. From time to time, we received unsolicited room service late at night – such as delivery of laundry – and occasionally no water ran from the taps. 'It will be there by the time you get back to your room,' we were told at the bureau. Indeed it was, contained in a bucket by the doorway. When breakfast was not ready at the time the restaurant doors were due to open, the doorman would instruct guests in a powerful voice to 'Go to your room!'. At breakfast, as we were presented with an impressively large menu, the steward would invariably enquire 'with or without egg?', for this was the only choice. There was a well-attended bar in the evenings, the most popular drink among the Nigerians being Guinness. Posters on the walls of the bar advertised Guinness as giving 'power', symbolized by a flexed arm with clenched fist, and 'plenty power' was a much-prized possession. 'Harp' lager, brewed in Benin City by Guinness, was generally preferred by the few expatriates. A band played 'heavy funk' in the hotel grounds at night, and its deep 'pop' rhythm boomed away well into the small hours.

Not unexpectedly, housing suitable for expatriates was extremely difficult to obtain. We were very fortunate in having our house located and secured in advance by John Storey, who had been reassigned from Kano and had many years experience of living and working in Nigeria. It was handed over directly to me by the outgoing occupant who was also a staff member of a UN Agency. Had there been a gap of even a day, I may have lost the opportunity to have it. During the hand-over, I took over his very old boxer dog, 'Carmelia'. The house – No. 139, Aiguobasimwin Crescent – was rented through the private sector, but hard, and most soft, furnishings were provided by the government. It was a large two-storey building with four bedrooms, two bathrooms, three toilets, a verandah at the front and back at ground floor level, and two verandahs on the second floor, each leading from separate bedrooms. It stood in a large plot of ground adjacent to one of the fairways of the Benin City golf course, in an attractive setting with a spacious drive set around a fine flamboyant tree in the front garden. There were French doors, louvre windows and terrazzo laid floors and stairs. It had an air of past greatness and decadence that would have been appropriate in a Somerset Maugham novel. It badly needed redecoration and also some restoration. During the first day in the house, I was tied up with work, while Irene learnt the internal geography of the building and shopped for groceries and basic household utensils to suffice until our personal effects arrived from South Africa. This was just as well, for otherwise we may have begun to get some badly needed restoration done, including to the somewhat shaky scaffolding supporting the outdoor overhead water cistern. Fortunately we did not, for that night, soon after midnight, a burglar started to climb up the scaffolding. We could hear his slow progress up the framework of galvanized iron piping. Since, at that time, we had no idea how many intruders were involved and whether or not they were armed, we concentrated on blocking entry through our two bedroom doors, using all the moveable furniture in the room. 'Carmelia' was no use at all; she just hid under the stairs. Just as the intruder reached the level of one of the windows to the outside landing, the scaffolding must have swung loose from the top of the wall, for there was a loud crash, followed by a curse, as he fell onto the ground. We saw him as he ran away down the front drive and, as he passed below our window, he picked up a stone and threw it in our direction. Next morning I contacted the police who came straight away. One officer noted the dirty hand prints close to the piping and up the wall and remarked, 'There have not been serpents; there has been a human presence'. I took this remark to be in no way casual, for within Southern Nigeria we were living in an area where a culture of animism and paganism existed concurrently with Christianity and, to a much lesser extent, Islam.

Within days, it became clear that, in spite of the warmth, charm and tremendous sense of humour exhibited by the many Nigerians that I met and talked to, we were living in unsettled times. It must be remembered that, less than ten years ago, there had been bloody battles between the tribes, largely Ibo, living in the south-eastern part of Nigeria and the tribes of Islamic faith, notably the Hausa, living in northern Nigeria. The attempts by the Ibo to form a separate country, Biafra, had failed and, in 1970, they surrendered. The country was presently under a federal military government, headed by Lieutenant-General Olusegun Obasanjo, whose most senior officers were mostly of the Islamic faith. There was a large military presence in Bendel State and it was rumoured that some of the many burglaries and acts of violence, including rape and shooting, were carried out at night by military personnel dressed in civilian clothing. A few weeks after our arrival, two newly arrived expatriate staff of the University of Benin had their home broken into. The husband was shot in the hand and his young wife was so frightened that they left their house the following day, leaving behind all their possessions, including their car. They returned to England by the earliest flight and never came back to Nigeria.

Within a fortnight, Irene and I turned the house into a home. We employed a maid, Caroline, and a garden boy, Dick, both Ibos, and with their help patched up woodwork that had been damaged by termites. We dusted, scrubbed and polished, but were never able to dispel completely the slightly decrepit appearance of the rooms, caused by moulds thriving in the hot, humid atmosphere indoors and the reddish staining on the floors created over the years by thick layers of desert dust brought in daily during December to February, the period of the Harmattan winds. Within a few days of Christmas, we reduced the infestations of cockroaches, silverfish and sugar ants in the kitchen cupboards and painted the kitchen. The small lizards, present in almost every room, were allowed to stay, as their presence indoors was believed, locally, to be a sign of good fortune. The electric pump that raised the water up to the outdoor overhead cistern was repaired, and the geyser overhauled that provided hot water to the wash basin and bath upstairs. A re-conditioned air-conditioner, supplied by the government, was fitted into the wall of our bedroom, and I installed a burglar alarm downstairs that operated from a radio signal from the bedroom. One day shortly after Christmas, a lorry drew up in front of the house and deposited all our personal effects from South Africa. The crates were untampered with and the contents in perfect condition.

In addition to the few paintings and prints, we hung several pieces of bark on the wall, with orchids growing on them. The invariably hot and humid atmosphere in the lounge was perfect for their growth and, periodically, we obtained some very fine displays of flowers.

Within a few days of our arrival in Benin City, I took over leadership of the project for some fifteen months, as well as commencing the entomological work. During this period, the infrastructure was built up for carrying out laboratory and field work, housing staff, and providing project transport. These facilities were established in three centres of operation, each one sited in a different ecological stratum. The Benin City centre gave access to the rain forest and also acted as HQ. The centre at Auchi, nearly ninety miles north of Benin City, gave access to derived savannah with relict forest, and the centre at Sapele, about forty miles south of Benin City, provided the strata of urban and peri-urban situations. In the course of building up the infrastructure, I met many Nigerian officials and businessmen. Almost without exception, they were extremely pleasant conversationalists with a strong sense of humour and shared the British capacity to laugh at themselves. In Nigeria, there was also a strong tradition of freedom of expression, both in the written and in the spoken word, and this was most refreshing after being exposed to strongly government-influenced media in the other African countries. Administrative progress was, however, often agonisingly slow, as officials were quite often 'not on seat', and repeated visits to their offices were usually necessary to resolve almost any matter. The principal requirements for success were the patience of Job and the ability to withstand the heat. On one occasion, administrative matters were not discussed until the official had liberally splashed each corner of his well-furnished room with whisky to appease the spirits. I could not help noting that he used a good single malt, but it was clearly not the time to ask him if a less expensive brand would have sufficed. I had the impression that government administration within the Bendel State, apart from the sometimes conflicting requirements between the Federal and State Governments, was far from simple. There appeared to be a slight undercurrent of paganism whereby an official, more junior in administration but more senior in pagan society, could influence decisions of a more senior official. I was told that such persons could sometimes be identified by talismans such as rings of a certain type on their fingers. I was glad to hand over the leadership of the project to a colleague, Dr Hernando Cardenas, at the end of March 1978, and give full attention to the mosquitoes and transmission of malaria in the different ecological strata. Dr Cardenas continued to build up the project so that, by early 1980, there were six WHO staff, three Nigerian professional, and sixty-two other national staff.

As I was based in Benin City, I was able to take more part in collection of mosquitoes from the forest stratum than from those related to Auchi and Sapele. In October 1977, Nigerian Federal Government entomologist, Miss C.N. Enelamah, joined the project and shared the work with me. I enjoyed going out into the field, collecting mosquitoes and bringing them into the laboratory for examination and dissection. Experience had taught me that, tedious though it may sometimes be, collecting mosquitoes frequently oneself, and not leaving the work largely to much more junior collectors, brings a valuable feel and understanding of the subject which is otherwise missed. Personal observations of the conditions under which mosquitoes live, and conversations with local people, sometimes reveal circumstances or local customs which bring mosquito and people together, or even move them apart, in an unexpected way.

Mosquitoes in the different ecological strata showed interesting and important differences from the point of view of malaria transmission. In the forest, in addition to the main vector *Anopheles gambiae*, several other species of *Anopheles* flourished with each species being associated with specific habitats within the forest, such as swampland or riverine grassland. In the derived savannah, *Anopheles gambiae* and *Anopheles funestus*, the two main vectors of Africa south of the Sahara occurred in about equal numbers, with the former being associated with the wet season and the latter with the dry one. In the urban areas, provided by Sapele township, the most common species was *Anopheles arabiensis* which is normally associated with very dry areas such as occur in northern Nigeria but it seemed that the urban environment provided a man-made desert. Most mosquito breeding in Sapele occurred in the estimated forty-five miles of drainage ditches bounding each side of the roads within the town. Not only were they the breeding sites of *Anopheles arabiensis*, but also of prodigious numbers of culicine mosquitoes which were such a nuisance that many of the town houses had their principal bedroom windows blocked to reduce the numbers entering their houses at night. There was some resistance among the malaria vectors to chlorinated hydrocarbon insecticides and, since no systematic insecticidal control measures against malaria vectors had been used in these areas, it seemed that the resistance had largely arisen from widespread use of these compounds in agriculture. Also, the more than occasional use of insecticide for illegal fishing may have been a contributory factor.

A very important aspect of our project's activities was training staff so that they could manage the work themselves when the project was eventually handed over to government. I gave frequent lectures and demonstrations in the laboratory of our Benin City headquarters, and a few also at the University of Benin and at the Federal Ministry of Health in Yaba, near Lagos. The problem of going by car was that the road, some thirty miles from Lagos, was unsafe. A European doctor was shot, his Mercedes car stolen and later used in a bank robbery in Benin City. Cars were sometimes stopped and stolen, and the occupants killed, either with machetes or by placing a tyre, saturated in petrol, around their necks. This macabre type of assassination was initially called 're-tyring' by the perpetrators, and then later on was more widely referred to as 'necklacing'. When we travelled by road, we almost invariably went in a convoy of at least two project vehicles. Occasionally, we flew from Benin City to Lagos. While the flights were not dangerous, there were frequently more boarding passes issued at Lagos than seats on the plane, an error sometimes compounded by misleading announcements about aircraft arrivals and departures. Corruption had been developed into an art form in Nigeria.

The public services, notably of water and electricity, were irregular. In order to maintain supplies to the laboratory, a WHO portable electricity generator and water bowser were kept in readiness at the Benin City HQ. Electric power failed frequently at home during the early months after our arrival. Dick would remark 'NEPA', which officially stood for 'Nigeria Electric Power Authority' but was generally understood to mean 'No Electric Power Again'. After many visits to the usually overcrowded NEPA office, we managed to have our electricity supply moved from the existing cable onto the military governor's line. Thereafter, the situation was greatly improved except when the sagging cables, in front of the house, touched during high winds and emitted a shower of sparks before power failed. Dick would then telephone NEPA shouting, 'Danger, explosion!', and NEPA staff would come in due course and attend to the lines. The electric wiring was so poor indoors that several electric bulbs would burn out each day, so we kept a large sack of spare bulbs in reserve. When the water supply failed, the overhead cistern was soon exhausted and we would fill up jerry-cans from a stand-pipe in town, pouring the water into the downstairs bath which we kept as a reservoir. Our sole air-conditioner was never very efficient but, even so, stepping outside the bedroom was like walking into a steam bath. Once it broke down and we were unable to get a replacement for over six months.

Reluctantly, Irene and I decided that it would not be wise to have our daughters out for their holidays as living conditions at home would be extremely uncomfortable for them. Neither did we have a high enough level of security in and around the building. We were also influenced by the amount of violence in the area, especially after the seven-year-old son of a European living in the area had been decapitated by a servant who had recently been dismissed by his master. However, we took great care to see our children at least once a year, either through home leave passages or at our own expense. Flying time was only a few hours between Lagos and Gatwick, which was a mere one and a half hours by road from Bexhill. On arrival, we did little except bask in the wonderful summer weather and sea air. In 1979 my leave was extended by six weeks, divided equally between the London School of Hygiene and Tropical Medicine and the University of Rome, to learn cytotaxonomic techniques used in identifying sibling species of mosquitoes. I was very pleased to have the opportunity to acquire these skills, but found the daily return train and tube journey between Bexhill and London extremely boring. Irene was more than happy to have the extra time at home. In Rome the study period was also most useful and the visit there was made pleasurable by seeing friends from our Arusha days, now working for FAO. Irene and I also nearly walked our legs off to see the magnificent Basilica and old Roman ruins.

It has been my experience that social life abroad is at its best when there is a circle of good friends of different nationalities; and so it was in Benin City. Irene and I had a wonderful time at weekends. As well as fellow countrymen, our friends included Greeks, Lebanese, Indians, Nigerians, Americans and Russians. On Friday evenings we usually had dinner followed by a game of bridge, often with three or four tables. Most of our friends' houses were fully air-conditioned and it was bliss to visit them. It would not have been practical, except at exorbitant expense, to air-condition our lounge and dining room because of the faulty louvre windows and the large stair-well leading to an open upstairs landing. Nevertheless, our friends were most tolerant and we had convivial evenings at our home, even including quite lively dancing. We had splendid Christmas parties at the home of Don and Bridget Jux. Bridget was a marvellous hostess and she and Irene became great friends, which made life for both of them far more pleasant than it might otherwise have been. Irene and I had our twenty-fifth wedding anniversary in Benin City and our friends, Wendy and Mike Reilly, gave a magnificent surprise party for us in their house.

One Saturday, in 1979, when Irene and I were in the middle of a small lunch party, Dr (Prince) I.S. Mebitaghan, Bendel State Ministry of Health Senior Consultant Epidemiologist, unexpectedly appeared at the door, looking extremely angry and distressed. 'Why did you not tell me that a case of smallpox has just been detected in Bendel State?' he demanded. His concern appeared quite justified since it was thought that the last case of smallpox had been detected in Somalia in 1977 and that the disease had been eradicated from the world. I knew nothing about this supposed case but assured him that I would look into it immediately; by Monday the information was at hand. It seemed that, while in Lagos, a young British expatriate, who had very recently arrived in Nigeria, had seen a notice indicating that smallpox had been eradicated. He then mentioned to an official there that he had recently been diagnosed in the Bendel State as having had smallpox. Prompt reaction followed, with WHO headquarters and Bendel State Ministry of Health being immediately advised. Further enquiry elicited that the young man had consulted a doctor in Bendel State about a skin condition and had been told that it was only a 'small small pox' – 'small small' in pidgin English simply meaning 'insignificant' or 'unimportant'. The false alarm was quickly and thoroughly investigated by a team from WHO headquarters in Geneva, who came to Bendel State and even visited me at home. It so happened that the last case was detected on 26th October 1977, and in May 1980, the World Health Organization concluded that smallpox had been eradicated from the world. It was a magnificent achievement accomplished very largely through the efforts of WHO, in which Dr D.A. Henderson had played a major part in ensuring its success.

There was always danger attached to being outdoors at night, but this did not prevent us from driving to and from our friends' houses, all of which, fortunately, were quite close by. However, one Friday night, after having played duplicate bridge at the home of Lila and Apu Nayar, we were returning home with a briefcase containing the playing cards, when we were stopped by two soldiers who waved us down with their rifles. They smelt strongly of drink and poked their rifles through one of the car windows. On spotting the case, they showed great interest and demanded to know what was in it. 'Playing cards', whispered Irene. One of the soldiers laughed with disbelief and roared to his companion, 'she says she has playing cards'. 'Open up that case', he shouted and Irene, with shaking hands, opened the case and all the plastic holders with their cards fell onto the floor of the car. The soldier thought this very amusing and said, 'She speak truth, they are playing cards'. He then banged the side of the car with his rifle and ordered us to drive on.

There was a good sports club in Benin City with facilities for tennis, golf and squash, all of which I played most weekends. Many of the Nigerian club members were very good tennis players and some of them extraordinarily keen. At least one court was usually occupied day and night, for advantage was taken of the overhead lighting and cooler conditions at night. Don Jux and I would frequently play three sets in the heat of the day, during which I would sweat away almost half a stone in weight. The club had two good squash courts donated by Guinness. They had corrugated iron roofs and no ventilation, so that temperatures inside must have exceeded a hundred degrees Fahrenheit. No wonder we usually found a few games sufficient. At golf, I had my first experience of playing on 'browns'. They varied enormously depending on the relative proportions of sand and diesel oil. Some were like sand-traps, or bunkers, while others resembled thick black treacle. I built a badminton court in our garden and soon discovered what an exhausting game that could be.

Although no school facilities were identified in Benin City to which Irene could offer help, for several months she provided much appreciated tuition to the daughter of a colleague who was unable to further her education in her home country of the Lebanon due to the prevailing civil war there. Irene advised one of our Indian friends on suitable boarding schools for her two daughters, as a consequence of which they both went to Ancaster House School in Bexhill where they were very popular and did well.

The club had a swimming pool which we occasionally visited, but I preferred to swim in the river at Sapoba some twenty miles away. Irene and I usually went with Don and Bridget and picnicked on the river bank. The water was crystal clear, cool, and a delight to swim in. The river must have been one of the old 'oil rivers' used by European traders in the nineteenth century. Their sailing ships came well up the rivers to obtain cargoes of oil-palm seeds which were used in the then burgeoning industry of soap manufacture. One of the principal goods for trading by barter was gin, transported in flat-sided bottles securely fitted into wooden cases. During my first visit to Sapoba, I saw a few of these case-bottles being offered somewhat passively for sale by two Africans sitting a little distance away from us on the edge of the river bank. There were no buyers and when I asked an expatriate, who regularly visited Sapoba, he said, 'People don't buy them because, as with every other artefact for sale in Nigeria these days, they are not genuine'. But genuine they were! One of the Africans took me out in a canoe. Within a few yards of the bank I could see several bottles lying on the river bed. On a small island a little further out, there were two small huts and, stacked outside them, hundreds of case-bottles. My African companion told me that these had all been collected from the river bed and within a short distance of the island. The river bed probably contained thousands of case-bottles, and all the oil rivers hundreds of thousands. On seeing the bottles, I thought of the ancient maritime saying 'one hand for the ship and one for yourself'. I also thought of the old ditty about 'ten green bottles hanging on the wall', for most were of green glass, although a few were brown. Many were in near-mint condition – no wonder most visitors to Sapoba thought they were not genuine! – but I found a mint one with a strand of petrified tissue paper sticking to it. The bottles were all moulded with their manufacturer's name and a few also with a trade mark. Typical of nineteenth century industry, the bottles were the products of numerous small manufacturers. Names included: E. Kiderlen; W. Hasekamp @ C.; C.W. Herwig; W.B. MacIver @ C.; J.J.W. Peters; van Marken @ Co.; v. Meerten @ C.; v. Hoytema @ C.; African, La Africana; African Association Ld. I bought a few bottles at thirty kobo each, and took one to the museum in Benin City. The official considered it very commonplace, an understandable view when seen against all the wonderful Nigerian tribal art on display there. He told me that no export permit was required and I still have them as mementoes.

Benin City is of great antiquity, its origins reaching back to the tenth century. It was the seat of the huge Empire of Benin that extended over much of West Africa for hundreds of years. The first ruler was a monarch, or 'oba', crowned about 1200 AD. Since then, there has been a continuity of obas for over eight hundred years, although the influence of the present day oba is largely ceremonial and within Bendel State. Even outside Africa, the name of Benin is widely associated with ancient Benin bronzes which were locally produced by the 'lost-wax' process, and which are still used in ceremonial practices at the palace of the oba within old Benin City. In 1978, the thirty-seventh oba, Akenzua II, died after forty-five years as ruling monarch. There was a period of deep mourning, particularly by the Edo (Bini) tribe. Many of them showed respect to their deceased monarch by shaving their heads, in response to a decree from the palace. Some members of other tribes living within Bendel State also shaved their heads as a mark of respect; those who did not were hounded and afraid to go outside their house at night. Even some expatriates shaved their heads, but I consulted Dr. (Prince) Mebitaghan and was advised that this was not necessary for staff of the WHO team who were not Edo. Rumours abounded, one being that the deceased oba would have to be buried along with forty human heads. From time to time the local newspapers would report that a headless human body had been found. Fear built up among people living in the locality to the extent that for several weeks streets were empty after dusk. There were even reports of headless dogs being found. The coronation took place of the thirty-eighth oba, Akenzua III, in March 1979, and was attended by many officials from government and of the palace of Benin. Some wonderful photographs were released of the newly crowned oba in traditional regalia and holding the ancient and famous two-bladed sword of office. Even then there were rumours, one of which was that the long ceremonial ritual involved a portion of the deceased's heart being eaten by the new heir to the throne.

I was reassigned to Geneva headquarters in March 1980. There was the usual round of farewell parties, gifts to our servants, selling the car extremely cheaply, packing and shipping personal effects. The junior entomological staff were overwhelmingly grateful because I had managed to get them onto the permanent staff of the Ministry of Health so that they would be guaranteed employment when the project eventually came to an end. They gave me a carved wooden plaque depicting Benin figures of antiquity; the oba dressed in all his regalia and holding his sword of office; the mythological Giant and Greedy Hunter; and one of the priests appeasing the spirits by sacrificing slaves, shown by a severed head and the priest holding up the upper part of a mutilated body.

Epilogue

Although I had spent eight months in Geneva some seven years ago, I still felt a bit strange living in a well-organized city, but Irene thrived in its sophisticated life style. Rented accommodation was difficult to obtain, a contributory factor being the presence of several embassies and large international organizations within Geneva township. We spent three months in the Longchamps Hotel before moving into an apartment that became available on the retirement of a staff member of the International Labour Organization who was returning to his home country of Ghana. It was a large apartment, with three bedrooms, two bathrooms, as well as a nice living room and kitchen. There was an underground garage and, as in all new buildings in Geneva, an atomic shelter, divided into store rooms one of which was allocated to our apartment. The Ghanaian couple had furnished the apartment most attractively and, as the apartment was to be rented unfurnished Irene and I bought many of their furnishings, including a fine Scandinavian table and chairs and cupboards, satin curtains and a king-sized bed. We bought a three-piece-suite in Louis XV style from a nearby shop and carpets from the 'Grand Passage', a large multiple store in the town centre. The apartment was on the fifth floor over the Co-op in Rue Daubin, thus making day-to-day shopping very easy for Irene and providing me with only a fifteen minute drive to work. Once again I was struck by the high standards of Swiss politeness, punctuality, efficiency, integrity and the cool, ordered manner with which they carried out any business or official matters. All these attributes, combined with the magnificent Swiss landscape, a wide spectrum of sporting activities, excellent restaurants, and a stable currency, made Switzerland a much sought after country in which to live and work. While I considered myself most fortunate to be stationed in Switzerland

Epilogue

until retirement, there were more than a few occasions when I missed the sights and smells of the African countryside and boisterous conversations with African staff and villagers.

Rue Daubin was situated in the Charmilles area of Geneva and had a certain village atmosphere. Irene, whose French became quite fluent through attending French conversation classes held weekly at the Women's Guild, became acquainted with many of the local people and enjoyed chats with them as she shopped in the Co-op or nearby. She made many friends in Geneva through her interest in playing bridge and through her membership of the Women's Guild at the Church. She was also a member of the United Nations Women's Guild and supervised and taught bridge at their meetings held weekly in the ILO headquarters building. Bridge parties were also held at members' homes. In this way, Irene developed a large circle of lady friends of many nationalities. The bridge parties provided a model of how people of different nationalities could not only get along, but also truly enjoy one another's company. I joined a squash club within easy walking distance of the WHO building and often had a few games during the lunch break. I also played weekend tennis, including winter tennis in a 'bubble', at a club near Petit Sacconnex.

Although some people described Lac Leman, or Lake Geneva, as the sewer of Switzerland, I, along with hosts of others, enjoyed swimming in it during the summer months. Irene and I would sometimes go to the lido, the 'bains de pacquis', on Saturday morning. I would swim, and then we would have the 'plat du jour' and 'trois de blanc' at the restaurant there, feeding the ducks and swans with pieces from our crusty rolls of bread. We became well-known to the people who managed the restaurant because they also worked, during the winter season (i.e. October to March), at the sports centre at Vernets where I enjoyed the magnificent Olympic-sized pool and skated on the indoor ice-rink. The Centre Sportif de Vernets was only a short distance from Rue Daubin, and Irene and I went there most Saturday mornings in the winter. I liked skating against the background of music, and after about two hours felt well exercised and ready to take Irene to lunch at a restaurant within the Centre which was designed to resemble a Swiss chalet, complete with synthetic geraniums and ivy. It even had an automaton Swiss band that could be activated by a coin. We ate out most weekends, there being an enormous choice of restaurants in the town, all of which served good food, no matter at what price level. We enjoyed walks in the lovely parks by the lake and in the well-preserved old town. Sometimes we went for drives into the scenic countryside but, after years of looking at murram road surfaces for corrugations, pot holes, rocks or other hazards, I was rarely at ease when driving in heavy traffic on autoroutes. Our daughters came over for some of their holidays and many of our friends, living abroad, took the opportunity to stop over in Geneva and visit us.

Geneva lies within a roughly horseshoe-shaped ring of mountains formed by the Jura to the north and the Saleve to the south. This configuration led to fumes from traffic, central heating systems, and factories stagnating over the town and causing atmospheric pollution in the more central areas, including Rue Daubin. This was reflected by acidic grime on the window panes and deposits of soot building up quite quickly around the edges of the windows of the apartment. Many people took to the fresh air of the Swiss countryside whenever the opportunity arose, but Irene and I chose that of Bexhill-on-Sea, and my leave entitlements were spent in many short breaks, sometimes only long weekends, at our seaside flat. We could get from our apartment in Geneva to our Bexhill flat in about three hours, the time being equally divided between air and road. This was all very convenient, particularly when making the wedding and reception arrangements in Bexhill for our daughters. In August 1982, Diana married Neil Rosser, a friend she had met some years earlier when she was at the 'Ox and Cow' and he was an undergraduate at Oriel college. In July 1984, Linda married Mark Thomas, whom she had met at Southampton University, also some years earlier, when they were both working for their Ph.D. degrees.

It was a great privilege to be working at WHO headquarters and to be able to continue the fight against malaria by playing a part in development of new methods and even revival of old ones that had lapsed since modern insecticides had come into widespread use. My duties included participating in expert committee meetings. These were stimulating, as experts from national governments and research institutions, as well as those drawn from WHO staff, took part together in the consultations. The technical reports arising from these meetings were in great demand, not only by national health authorities but also by training and research institutions.

Since insecticides were still the principal means by which insect and other arthropod-borne diseases were controlled, it was important that there should be an up-to-date manual from WHO dealing with this subject. I was assigned the task of revising the previous edition, which had been published in 1970. It was a demanding one, for a much wider range of insecticides and dosages had now to be included to provide for increased insecticide resistance in different vectors and pests in different parts of the world. Much consideration was given to the safe use of these pesticides, both to humans and to the environment, and the chapter on this subject was revised from the previous edition, to take the new insecticides into account. The revised edition was published by WHO in 1984.

Considerable professional and public concern existed over the wide and large scale use of some insecticides. One of the major impediments to the control of disease vectors was now insecticide resistance which, detected in only two arthropods of public health importance in 1947, had risen to one hundred and fifty five by 1980. Public concern related to environmental damage caused by pesticides, although this largely stemmed from agricultural usage. To reduce dependence on chemical pesticides and counter the development of insecticide resistance, WHO gave increasing attention to alternative methods of vector control. Before the synthetic insecticide era, environmental control measures, such as swamp drainage, realigning stream beds and intermittent irrigation played an important part in malaria control and some outstanding achievements were obtained. In recent times, there have also been notable successes with environmental control measures as in the construction of modern shipping to prevent rodent infestation and of certain airports to virtually exclude vector mosquito breeding. Since there was a great need for a published guide on this method of control, I joined ten other authors in contributing to a 'WHO manual on environmental management for mosquito control – with special emphasis on malaria vectors', which was published in 1982.

While environmental control may be the ideal and ultimate

solution to vector control, the initial capital outlay is sometimes very expensive and far more difficult to fund by governments than recurrent annual expenditure on chemical methods of control. Except in emergencies, when chemical methods alone may have to be used, a more practical and cost-effective method over the long term is usually offered by integrated vector control which involves environmental management, biological control methods and use of pesticides, but with less dependency on the latter. I spent several months working on various aspects of integrated vector control including preparation of working papers, taking part in an expert committee meeting on this subject, and assisting in the preparation of the Technical Report published in 1983.

Demographic studies show that the world population is growing and that it has risen from two and a half billion in 1950 to nearly four billion in 1985, and is expected to exceed six billion by the year 2000. Concurrently, a greater proportion of the world's population is living in urban areas. For example, it has been estimated by WHO that in 1950 just over 28 per cent were living in urban areas compared with 39% in 1975, and that nearly half the world's population will be living in urban areas by the year 2000. In view of the growing importance of urban vector control, my director Dr Norman Gratz and I, with the help of the WHO expert advisory panel, WHO staff members and outside consultants, carried out a detailed survey of municipal vector and rodent control services in twenty-six cities, most of which were in developing countries. The findings showed that malaria was being transmitted in 50 per cent of the cities surveyed and that 85 per cent of them had a serious pest problem with mosquitoes. Urban growth was found to be taking place so fast that it was far outstripping the rate at which essential health services were supplied. Extending over many of the urban areas were accumulations of water in blocked roadside ditches and stormwater drains; pools of stagnant water often contaminated with sullage discharges; and vast amounts of rubbish in the form of small containers, including plastic ones, capable of holding water in the rainy seasons. Much of vector breeding was therefore associated with lack of piped water, inadequate liquid and solid waste disposal and management, insufficient cleaning of open city storm drains, and lack of screening of latrines and septic tanks against mosquito breeding. Following this survey, several urban vector control projects were established based on environmental control measures and community participation. An expert committee on urban vector and pest control was held in 1987 which I attended as temporary adviser to WHO.

Following an international conference held at Alma-Ata in the USSR in 1978, the World Health Organization, in 1981, adopted the concept of primary health care, which 'is essential health care made universally accessible to individuals and families in the community by means acceptable to them, through their full participation and at a cost that the community and country can afford'. In conformity with this approach, WHO priority in development of methods of vector control was given to simple, safe, appropriate and inexpensive measures that could be used at individual or community level by members of the community themselves. I gave much thought to this subject but was largely uninspired until coming across an article by G.R. Port and P.F.L. Boreham in the then current issue of the *Bulletin of Entomological Research*, describing experimental hut results in which even torn bed-nets gave the sleeper significant protection from the bites of the malaria vector *Anopheles gambiae*. On considering this finding, along with my own much earlier ones on the effects of the synthetic pyrethroid insecticide, tetramethrin, on mosquitoes entering experimental huts, the idea occurred to me that bed-nets, treated with permethrin or another synthetic pyrethroid insecticide, might provide better protection against mosquitoes and, if used on a large enough scale, give a whole community good protection against malaria. In December 1982, recommendations were made by the directors of WHO collaborating centres and by the Expert Committee on Integrated Vector Control for trials to be carried out on bed-nets impregnated with pyrethroid insecticides. Following good results being obtained from an experimental hut trial, field studies on this possible method of control commenced in many countries. I went out to the Gambia in November 1984 to assist Dr Brian Greenwood, director of the medical research laboratory at Fajara, in drafting a protocol for a 1985 village-trial with permethrin treated bed-nets. It is understood that bed-nets impregnated with pyrethroid are now used in many developing countries and by millions of people as an anti-malaria measure with the unanticipated, but much-appreciated additional benefit of providing protection against the bites of bed-bugs.

The World Health Organization publishes the International Health Regulations, which play an extremely important part in reducing the international spread of diseases, and which include provisions for ridding aircraft of insects, using methods recommended by WHO. One of the duties assigned to me on arrival at Geneva was 'aircraft disinsection'. My first impression was that this would be a simple and minor assignment largely involving replying to queries from outside WHO concerning well-documented procedures for spraying the interior of an aircraft by means of aerosol dispensers to kill any insects that had inadvertently entered the aircraft. This initial impression was far from the reality. The subject was complex, difficult and quite time-consuming, but slowly developed into a most fascinating one, taking me to new countries and situations.

I was soon involved in updating the WHO recommendations for disinsecting aircraft. Any proposed new methods or insecticide formulations had to pass the most stringent scrutiny for they had to be safe to crew and passengers and not cause them undue discomfort; be unharmful to the fabric and equipment of the aircraft and also to the baggage and cargo in it; and also had to avoid all risk of fire. I was secretary of an informal WHO consultation on the disinsecting of vessels and aircraft, held in Geneva in November 1984, which recommended a further aerosol formulation for use in aircraft disinsection and, for the first time, a residual insecticide formulation of permethrin as an alternative to the use of insecticide aerosols. It was considered that the proposed use of the residual insecticide formulation would reduce the risk of any adverse effects on crew or passengers that has sometimes, although infrequently, been attributed to the inhalation of insecticide aerosols. I was also involved in a WHO-supported project to find a more environmentally friendly substitute for chloroflorocarbon propellents which were then widely used in aerosol formulations.

There has been an enormous increase in international travel during the last twenty years, heightening the risk of conveying insect vectors of malaria and other diseases, and even of the diseases themselves, from one country to another. This has happened in the past, a notable example being the establishment of *Anopheles gambiae* in Brazil in 1930, and its eradication from that country by 1940 following a protracted and intensive campaign. An important current concern was that a vector of malaria might be introduced and established in non-malarious countries and areas of the Pacific Islands, for there is a vast area of the Pacific where no malaria occurs. The *anopheline*-free area includes New Zealand and the Polynesian island groups of Samoa, Tonga, Cook, Tokelau, Tuvalu, Niue and Society; the Micronesian islands of Kiribati and Nauru; the Caroline and Marshall Islands; and New Caledonia and Fiji in Melanesia. In 1982, at the request of the WHO Western Pacific regional office, I visited several malarious and non-malarious countries in the Pacific to assess the risk of *anopheline* species being accidentally introduced and established in areas in which they were presently absent, and to advise on preventive measures to reduce the risk. It was an arduous, but most interesting, six weeks assignment, involving eighteen international and four inter-country flights, but greatly facilitated by my travelling with hand luggage only. Duty visits were made to airports and ports in The Philippines, Indonesia, Papua New Guinea, Solomon Islands, Vanuatu, Fiji, Australia, Nauru and Guam, and I met a total of one hundred and forty three officials – usually one or two at a time. Many places were inspected and much information gathered, leading to detailed technical recommendations. However, the risk of malaria vectors being introduced and established in areas in which they were presently absent, was generally judged to be low because nearly all international flights from the *Anopheles*-infested countries in the Pacific still arrived and departed in daytime, but, unless tighter control measures were adopted, this risk would be expected to increase if night-time departures became more frequent.

It was interesting to speculate why *anophelines* had not spread over the whole of the Pacific in the historical past, for they had presumably had at least thousands of years in which to have done so. No clear explanation emerged, but climatic and oceanographic data indicated that transportation of *anopheline* mosquito adults from the north-western islands in the Pacific, where they occur, to south-eastern islands in which they are absent, would have been seriously inhibited by distance, combined with the strong winds which blow from the south-east for most of the year. The possibility of immature stages of *anophelines* being carried from the north-western to the south-eastern islands would appear even more remote. They would not have been able to survive long exposure to pure sea water and, if conveyed in small natural containers holding fresh water, the powerful sea currents that flow from east to west in the equatorial zone would have taken them in the opposite direction.

Although my brief concerned mosquito vectors of malaria, I soon became aware of the prodigious numbers of the arbovirus vector mosquito, *Aedes aegypti*, breeding within several seaports; and vast numbers of another arbovirus vector, *Aedes albopictus*, also breeding in one of them. The problem seemed to be associated with the widespread use of container transport. At a distance the containers may look like matchboxes, but close to they are the size of a garage and the giant vehicles for lifting them have tyres some two metres in diameter. Their old tyres were found on nearly every wharf inspected and most of them contained water infested with *Aedes* larvae. Infested tyres were sometimes found only a short distance away from a docked ocean-going vessel. There were also great numbers of small boats lying off the ports, and most of them had at least one old (although much smaller) tyre hanging over their sides for use as a buffer when coming into port. These conditions seemed to present a continued risk of international transportation of the *Aedes* species and required further attention to vector control. It was an extremely difficult problem well known to the WHO Western Pacific regional office, but I felt it would do no harm to mention these findings in my assignment report since *Aedes albopictus*, which had been introduced into the Solomon Islands in 1978, had been responsible for an outbreak of Dengue fever in Honiara as recently as 1982, in fact only a few months before my visit there. Back in Europe, the subject of the disinsecting of vessels and aircraft became of timely interest just before the consultation on this subject held by WHO in Geneva in November 1984, for *Aedes albopictus*, or the 'tiger' mosquito, had only a few weeks previously been discovered breeding in Memphis, Tennessee. It was thought to have been possibly introduced into the USA through infested vehicle tyres.

In June 1985, I visited the Tropical Pesticides Research Institute in Arusha, Tanzania, in connection with a WHO-supported village-scale trial of mosquito-coils. It was all very nostalgic. The T.P.R.I. staff were most welcoming and I even received an occasional smiling 'shikamoo', which was quite something twenty-four years after independence. The Institute had grown immensely for several large buildings, housing offices and laboratories, now stood in what was once a field of beans, alternating with maize, next to the old T.P.R.I. laboratories which were remarkably unchanged and still in use. We had a most enjoyable staff meeting in the new library and I gave a short talk about the World Health Organization and some recent developments in entomology. They in turn told me about their work and shortage of resources which impeded it. At the weekend, I was taken on a short trip to the Momella Game Reserve and Ngurdoto Crater. It was a pleasant drive but there was nothing like the amount or variety of game that I had seen some fifteen years previously, in spite of large notices here and there stating severe penalties for poaching. Arusha township looked pretty run-down, largely due to much of the exterior paintwork of the shops being old and scoured by dust-bearing winds. I stayed at the New Arusha Hotel which had not changed a great deal except for prices. Breakfast of egg on toast cost one hundred and twenty shillings and a small bottle of unlabelled beer cost one hundred and seventy five shillings – compared with about five shillings in 1972. I met several old friends and had dinner at their houses and drinks at the Arusha Gymkhana Club, and was able to make a small but welcome gift of a bar of Swiss chocolate to each of them. I walked round to my old home in Bara Bara ya Serengeti and was welcomed by the resident who kindly let me walk the garden. The beautiful roses were no more and half of the garden had been planted with beans. This was quite understandable since wages were unable to keep pace with inflation and many gardens were now planted with food crops which were largely sold to supplement income. I flew to Geneva from Kilimanjaro International Airport and was happy to see young expatriates, some with small children, full of enthusiasm for their new postings in Tanzania.

I contributed to other WHO technical publications, including ones on rift valley fever, arthropod- and rodent-born viral diseases, resistance of vectors to pesticides, a guide for the control of emergencies caused by yellow fever, and also to the *United Nations High Commissioner for Refugees Handbook for Emergencies*. Duty visits were also made to other countries including Bulgaria, the Federal Republic of Germany, India, Russia, Senegal and Turkey. In 1982, the London School of Hygiene and Tropical Medicine awarded me the Ademola Medal, jointly with Dr. Robert Kaiser, one of the senior staff of CDC, Atlanta, USA, 'for outstanding achievements in health in the tropics'. I retired four years later after working overseas for thirty-six years, with a notable thirty of them in Africa, largely in the field.

Index

Index

Goodwin, Dr. L.G. 150
Gordon Smith, Dr. C.E. 150
Gratz, Dr. Norman 200
Gray, Dr. J.B. 150
Greenway, Peter 36
Greenwood, Dr. Brian 201
Griggs, Hilda 83, 84
Grogan, Colonel 64

Hammond, Les 106
Hampshire, Cyril 107
Hansford, Dr. Frank 166, 179
Haskell, Dr. Peter 150
Hedges, Tom 101, 113
Hemmingway, Bessie 74, 78
Hemmingway, Diane 74
Hemmingway, John 66, 74, 76
Hemmingway, Robert 74
Henderson, Dr. D.A. 192
Hocking, Professor Brian 130
Hocking, Dr. Kay 51, 83, 91, 99,
    100, 103, 104, 130, 133,
    137, 139, 140
Hocombe, Jill and Simon 122
Hofer, Max 100
Huddleston, John 74
Hurd, Dr. 77
Hutt, Sir Bruce 76

Insecticides 120, 139
    DDT 60, 90, 160, 161
    malathion 161
    pyrethrins 162
    pyrethroids 161, 201
    resistance to 81, 90, 120, 189,
        199, 206
Isige, Hosea 104
Ivens, Dr. Giles 89

Jacques, Bill 48
Jaeger, Professor Friz 133
Jones, Rev. Bryn 107, 109
Jones, Pat 114
Jordan, Dr. Peter 24
Jorgensen, Kirsten 177
Jux, Bridget 191, 193

Jux, Don 191–3

Kaiser, Dr. Robert 206
Kenyatta, President Jomo 142
Kitta, George 152
Kuentslinger, Mr 144

Laurie, Colonel William 24, 28,
    29, 32, 42, 56
Lee, Cliff 133
Lewthwaite, Dr. L. 15, 85
Lockhart, Edgar 178
London School of Hygiene and
    Tropical Medicine 14, 16,
    18, 50, 51, 190
Long, Mike 176
Long, Molly 110, 171, 176
Lush, Dr. Brandon S. 150

MacAskill, Marie 178
Macdonald, Professor S.G. 150
Mackenzie, 'Mac' 26
McKone, Colin 104
McLean, Dr. and Mrs 80
McLeod, Alistair 48
McMahon, J.J. 47
Macmillan, Tom 105
Maharali, Abdhul 99
Maji-maji 74
Malecela, John 115
Margaret, HRH Princess 79
Mataba, Chief Ntemi 30
Materu, Dr. Ephata 141, 153, 157
Mattingly, Peter 36
Mebitaghan, Dr. (Prince) I.S. 191,
    195
Medawar, Sir Peter 14
Medicine horn 71, 72
Messer, Peter 178
Miller, Wing Commander 'Dusty'
    48, 51, 102
Miller, Joan 102
Ministry of Overseas Development
    176
Mkwawa, Chief Adam Sapi, OBE 142

209

Wood, Michael A. 145
Woodruff, Professor A.M. 150
World Health Organization
(WHO) 76, 90, 120, 122,
155, 161, 163, 165, 166,
168, 179–81, 192, 198, 202,
205
    primary health care 201
    projects 166, 168, 181,
182, 200

technical reports 166, 199

Yeo, Doug 52
Y.M.C.A. 15, 17, 55
Y.W.C.A. 17

Zanzibar revolution 122, 136
Zoology 14